WORLD WITHOUT HUNGER

WORLD WITHOUT HUNGER

SECRETARY OF AGRICULTURE
ORVILLE L. FREEMAN

FREDERICK A. PRAEGER, PUBLISHERS
New York • Washington • London

FREDERICK A. PRAEGER, PUBLISHERS
111 Fourth Avenue, New York, N.Y., 10003, U.S.A.
77–79 Charlotte Street, London W.1, England

Published in the United States of America in 1968
by Frederick A. Praeger, Inc., Publishers

© 1968 by Frederick A. Praeger, Inc.

Library of Congress Catalog Card Number: 68-19222

Printed in the United States of America

To the pioneers
in agricultural technical assistance
who have struggled and persevered
to increase food production
on the far frontiers of the world

Acknowledgments

Much of the research on which this volume is based was done by the Department of Agriculture. I wish to acknowledge my colleagues in the Department who devote their lives to research with little recognition or credit. Without their work, realistic planning for the future would be impossible. Wayne D. Rasmussen, Martin E. Abel, Jane M. Porter, and Ernest G. Moore have been particularly helpful to me in making this book a reality. Without their understanding patience and their help in planning, researching, and editing, this book would not have been possible. Any mistakes are mine. Any credit should be theirs.

ORVILLE L. FREEMAN

Washington, D.C.
February, 1968

Preface

Not many months ago, I awoke in a cold sweat from a horrible nightmare. I had dreamed that the monsoon had failed in India, China was having a prolonged drought, the Soviet Union had suffered a major crop failure, and, in the United States, the wheat crop had been ruined by a new disease. Millions of people were starving all over the world. Little children with spindly legs and distorted bellies pointed their fingers at me and chanted over and over, "It's your fault, it's your fault." When the children in my dream died, they were replaced by others who kept chanting, "You are to blame."

This dream illustrates the shocking inadequacy of the world food situation and the awesome responsibility placed upon the United States as the major source of food reserves in the world. It also illustrates the dilemma of the U.S. Secretary of Agriculture.

Our agricultural productivity is growing much faster than our domestic demand. More Americans suffer from overeating than from lack of food. During the 1950's, we learned that unrestricted production, even with low price supports, results in enormous surpluses, particularly of grains. These surpluses are costly to maintain, and their existence works against achieving fair prices for producers. As a practical matter, we must manage our rapidly growing agricultural production, lest we smother in our own abundance.

But we have only to look around the world to see that things are badly out of balance. Millions of people in other countries are undernourished. Many go to bed hungry every night, and there are no food reserves to protect them against poor harvests. Yet, with the threat of growing hunger and starvation in the world, the United States has reduced its food production. This, the starving children in my dream could not understand.

The tragic thing about the world food problem is that it need not be—and it need not grow. We are dealing with a race between what could be done and what will be done, as much as with a race between population and food supply. We already have the knowledge and the resources to achieve the desired balance between food and people. What is lacking is the willingness to commit this knowledge and these resources to an all-out attack on hunger. Unless we call up the will to bring about a better balance between food and population, modern civilization will be racked by increasing turmoil and unrest; millions of people will be driven by the simple need to survive. When this happens, a world based on reason and reasoned action will be gravely threatened.

Who should produce the food for our hungry world?

This question comes to me over and over again. Efficient producers in many countries are quick to say that food production should be governed by the rule of comparative advantage, and that each geographic area should produce those things that it can grow or manufacture most efficiently. World trade, these people argue, will take care of distribution.

One flaw in this argument is that producers must be paid.

The efficient producers are concentrated in relatively few countries. Most of the people who lack food have neither the goods nor the money to pay for it. To date, the United States has been the only country willing to pay its own producers to grow food to give away in significant quantities over a sustained period. But, even with our large resources, we cannot afford to continue such a policy indefinitely. Moreover, it is very likely that exploding populations in the less developed countries will outrun the productive capacity of the United States and other developed nations before the turn of the century.

Instead of trying to feed the world, we must work at top speed and with tireless determination toward the only possible long-term answer: the bulk of the world's food must be produced where it is to be consumed. Countries with capital and know-how and countries with hungry people must form a partnership to mobilize the resources needed to increase total food production, whether through cultivating new lands or through increasing yields on existing farmlands. Meanwhile, we buy time with food aid. The problem facing us is more than national or regional; it is world-wide. Its solution demands a great international effort.

This book seeks to explore what you and I can do as individuals and what our nation and other nations must do as governments to free mankind from the threat of famine. It is written out of my conviction that, if all peoples work together, nightmares of starvation can be forgotten and we can realize the age-old, sweet dream of a world without hunger.

Contents

List of Charts

List of Tables

xv

WORLD WITHOUT HUNGER

❋

CHAPTER 1

The Problem—
Man and His Food Supply

❋

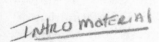

There has always been a food-population problem. Since the beginning of time, man has experienced food shortages, hunger, and starvation. This was just as true when civilization was confined to a few fertile valleys as it is now. But today the future of our entire civilization in an interdependent world is threatened.

Nearly 200 years ago, the Reverend Thomas Robert Malthus expounded the theory that population would increase until it outran the food supply; then, a major disaster, such as war or pestilence, would restore the natural balance. For many decades, it appeared that science, applied to farming, had overcome that threat. But, in recent years, some people have felt that Malthus' dire prediction was on the verge of fulfillment. There are 3.5 billion people on the earth today. Regardless of what is done about population control, there will be at least 1 billion more by 1980. Somehow, within a dozen years, the world must develop the capacity to feed at least 4.5 billion people.

We are in the midst of a population explosion. World population is estimated to have been 250 million at the beginning of the Christian era. It took fifteen centuries for the population to double; by 1600, the total was 500 million. The next doubling required only 225 years; world population reached 1 billion in 1825. It tripled during the next 135 years and reached 3 billion by 1960. Experts predict that, at present growth rates, world population will double again during the next 35 years, reaching 6 billion by the year 2000 (see Chart 1).

Since I have been Secretary of Agriculture, the total world population has grown by an estimated 400 million people, with over 250 million in the developing regions of the world alone. This pattern and rate of growth are more than equivalent to adding the population of the United States to that of the developing regions in just over five years, and have upset the already precarious balance between food and people. The result is a food gap, and is the reason that concerned people around the world have called for a war on hunger. They recognize that the situation is now approaching crisis dimensions and know that our generation must act to prevent this crisis; it will be too late for our children to do so.

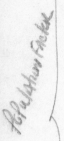

Two features of this food gap demand attention. One, of course, is the relationship of total population to the world's over-all capacity to produce food. The other is population distribution in relation to the food-producing capacity of the area where the population growth takes place. Both are equally important, but the most pressing, immediate difficulties stem from the increasing imbalance between population growth and food-producing capacity in particular areas.

The alarming fact is that the largest growth in population is taking place in regions already short of food. In 1920, about one-third of the world's population was located in what we

Chart 1

TWENTY CENTURIES OF
WORLD POPULATION GROWTH

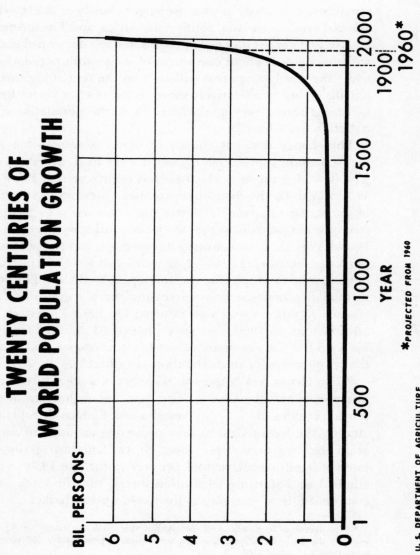

U. S. DEPARTMENT OF AGRICULTURE

*PROJECTED FROM 1960

can classify roughly as the more developed areas of the world
—North America, Europe, the U.S.S.R., and Oceania—and the
remaining two-thirds in what we might classify as the less developed areas—East Asia, South Asia, Africa, and Latin America. By 1980, based on present trends, today's developed areas
will contain only about one-fourth of the world's population,
while the developing areas will contain the remaining three-
fourths. Thus, in a relatively short period of sixty years, there
will have been a very marked change in the population distribution (see Chart 2).

The change that has already occurred is responsible for
highly complex problems of world-wide food distribution.
The flow of grain in world trade has been reversed. Prior to
World War II, the developing countries were net exporters
of grain; together, they exported, on a net basis, 11 million
tons of grain per year to the developed world. By the close of
World War II, these countries no longer had an export surplus of grain. During 1948–52, an average of 6 million metric*
tons of grain was shipped to the developing countries. The flow
in that direction has been increasing sharply ever since. It
reached 13 million tons a year during the 1957–59 period, 20
million tons in 1960, and an estimated 31 million tons in
1966. In the absence of an all-out effort to reverse this trend,
the prospects are for an acceleration (see Chart 3).

When Henry A. Wallace was Secretary of Agriculture, some
thirty years ago, the United States was one of three grain exporting regions. Both Latin America and Eastern Europe, including the Soviet Union, were exporting as much or more
grain than we were. Since then, North American grain exports of 5 million metric tons per year in the late 1930's have
climbed to a startling 60 million metric tons in 1966. Our
continent is now emerging as the world's bread basket.

---

* Measurements in metric tons throughout this book are based on figures
used by the United Nations. A metric ton equals approximately 205 pounds
more than a standard U.S. ton.

Chart 2

WORLD POPULATION BY GEOGRAPHIC REGIONS, WITH PROJECTIONS

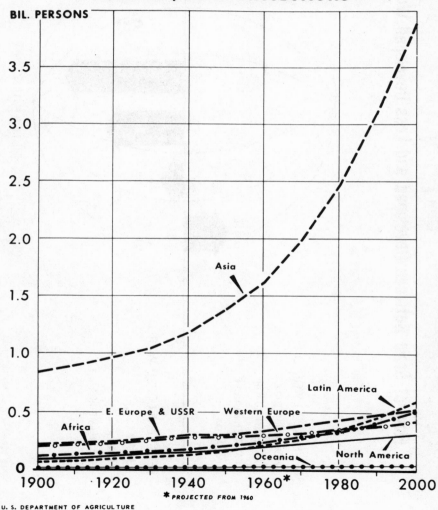

BIL. PERSONS

Asia

Latin America

E. Europe & USSR ——— Western Europe

Africa

Oceania

North America

1900   1920   1940   1960*   1980   2000

* PROJECTED FROM 1960

U. S. DEPARTMENT OF AGRICULTURE

Chart 3

Flow of Grain Between Developed and Less Developed World

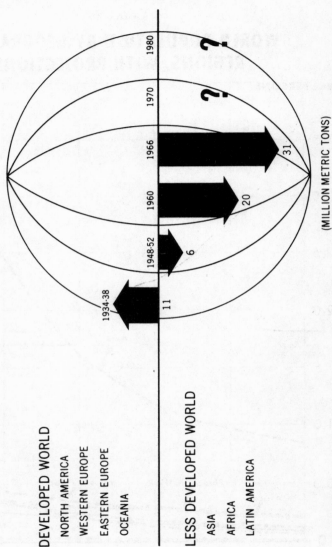

DEVELOPED WORLD

NORTH AMERICA
WESTERN EUROPE
EASTERN EUROPE
OCEANIA

LESS DEVELOPED WORLD

ASIA
AFRICA
LATIN AMERICA

(MILLION METRIC TONS)

1934-38   1948-52   1960   1966   1970   1980

11   6   20   31   ?   ?

U.S. DEPARTMENT OF AGRICULTURE

Nowhere during this period has the contrast between the economic systems of the Free World and the Communist countries been so evident as in agriculture. In 1957, Premier Khrushchev challenged us to economic competition. When I visited the Kremlin in 1963, and spent four hours discussing agriculture with him, he was still bragging. Today, the Russians are giving us stiff competition in several key areas. Steel production in the Soviet Union is projected to surpass that of the United States within a few years. Our lead in hydroelectric power generation is narrowing. We are not sure whether the first man on the moon will speak English or Russian. But in agriculture there is no contest. With about 5 per cent of our people on farms, we are producing enough grain for 200 million Americans, 60 million Indians, and the equivalent of 100 million people in other countries. The Russians, with 35 per cent of their workers still tied to the land, have been, until recently, dependent on grain imports from the outside world. (If we were as far ahead in the space race as we are in agriculture, we would be running a shuttle service to the moon by now.)

Much of the very rapid rate of growth in world population can be attributed to man's recently acquired ability to lower death rates drastically. Such killers as plague, cholera, smallpox, and diphtheria are on the wane. In addition, such debilitating diseases as malaria have been eliminated or reduced to negligible proportions over vast areas of the world. We can be proud of these accomplishments. But, ironically, in eliminating one type of human suffering we have increased the chances for another—hunger and starvation.

One answer to this sad contradiction is to reduce the number of births, just as we have reduced the number of unnecessary, early deaths. A study by the Food and Agriculture Organization of the United Nations (FAO) states:

The continuation of high fertility in the face of the reduction of mortality, particularly in the economically less advanced regions, is the crux of the population problem in the world today, and is an integral and essential factor in any realistic approach to the food outlook.

Just as man has been unwilling to live with a variety of diseases and a high mortality rate, so should he be unwilling to live with needlessly high birth rates. Demographers tell us that an average woman can bear about seven children during her lifetime. In most of the developing nations, the average number of children per woman has been between 4.5 and 6.0. Surveys in twenty-seven nations in all stages of development show that, even in the least developed of these nations and in the most traditional of societies, the average number of children desired by married couples is lower than the number actually being born. As people come to realize that they no longer need to have large numbers of children to ensure the survival of the family, they will become more and more receptive to family planning. Modern science has given us feasible means to regulate the birth rate, even in the lowest income areas.

Thus, in the long run, one of the most effective, though difficult, ways to deal with malnutrition and hunger is by control of population. A recent economic study of population-control efforts in developing countries, by Stephen Enke, Professor of Economics at Duke University, concludes:

(1) If economic resources of given value were devoted to retarding population growth, rather than accelerating production growth, the former resources could be 100 or so times more effective in raising *per capita* incomes in many less-developed countries. (2) An adequate birth-control programme in these countries might cost as little as 10 cents *per capita* yearly, equivalent to about 1 percent of the cost of current development programmes.

Prompt action is important in the countries that have had the greatest increase in population in the last twenty years, since they have the largest number of young women who will be bearing children in the next ten years. The difference between two children and six in a family may well determine whether we will live in a world of healthy, educated, productive people or one of widespread starvation and human degradation. Birth rates have already been reduced in many of the more developed areas of the world. In Europe, they are typically between 1.7 and 1.9 per 100 of the population; in the United States, 1.85. But the prevailing birth rate in most of Africa, Asia, and Latin America is 4 to 4.5 per cent.

We do not have to assume a continuation of past trends in population growth as inevitable. Revolutionary changes have taken place in the attitudes of governments and world opinion during the past decade. The leadership that the Asian nations have taken in advocating and initiating population-control programs is reassuring. Japan pioneered in this. Despite an already dense population, its birth rate had soared to 3.4 per cent in 1947. In 1948, the Japanese Government passed a law permitting abortions. By the mid-1950's, it was placing emphasis on contraception. Today its birth rate is about 1.7 per cent. The Government of India adopted a policy favoring population control as early as 1950 and has given it high priority since 1964. India hopes to lower its birth rate from about 4.0 per cent to 2.5 per cent by 1975. Ceylon, Korea, Hong Kong, Taiwan, Pakistan, and Thailand have all introduced at least experimental programs through a combination of government and private support. Strong interest is evident in Turkey, Malaya, the United Arab Republic, and Tunisia. Although not enough has been accomplished in nations with high birth rates, the situation is changing. Progress is being made.

The first step in the development of a population policy by the U.S. Government came in 1959, with the report of the President's Committee to Study the United States Military Assistance Programs, popularly known as the Draper Committee for its chairman, General William H. Draper. A section on population recommended that the United States "support studies and appropriate research leading to the availability of relevant information in a form most useful to individual countries in the formation of practical programs to meet the serious challenge posed by rapidly expanding population." Dwight D. Eisenhower, President at the time, did not share such a view and said that he could "not imagine anything more emphatically a subject that is not a proper political or governmental activity or function or responsibility."

Less than two years later, in March, 1961, President John F. Kennedy discussed the adverse effects of rapid population growth in his first foreign-aid message to Congress. Since that time, the Agency for International Development (AID) has become increasingly explicit in stating its willingness to advise on population problems when requested. By March, 1965, AID policy was not to volunteer assistance to other nations, but to consider requests for technical assistance to train family-planning workers, to make grants of local currencies for financing family-planning programs, and to provide equipment, including vehicles and educational aids. The United States was not then willing to provide contraceptives or the machinery for their manufacture.

In September, 1967, the first grant to a foreign country to buy contraceptives was announced by William A. Gaud, AID administrator. The grant, amounting to $1.3 million, was made to India. With this move, the United States completed a startling reversal in its official position on population control. Significantly, former President Eisenhower also changed his personal views. On October 26, 1963, in an article in the *Saturday Evening Post,* he stated:

Population control is a highly sensitive problem, of course. When I was President, I opposed the use of Federal funds to provide birth-control information to countries we were aiding because I felt this would violate the deepest religious convictions of large groups of taxpayers. As I look back, it may be that I was carrying that conviction too far.

It does us little, if any, good to provide economic or technical assistance to nations which show no concern for their population explosion.

The new attitudes toward population control, brought about largely by thousands of people working through voluntary organizations all over the world, lend encouragement to those who believe that famine can be prevented. If, in the remainder of this century, we can do no more than stabilize population, that halt in growth would be a big help toward bringing food production into balance with needs.

The people of a country are its most valuable resource. But this is an empty statement if the stork outruns the plow and the people are so debilitated by endemic or nutritional disease that they have little physical and intellectual energy. We are all moved to compassion by the pictures, all too familiar, of half-naked children with emaciated limbs and distended bellies from malnutrition.

At this moment the extent of malnutrition is staggering. Two-thirds of the world's people live in countries where average diets are nutritionally inadequate. They consume nearly one-third fewer calories per day than the U.S. average, 300 calories per day less than the 2,300 minimum required for normal activity and health. During the most recent Indian food crises, many people survived on 900 calories per day—100 calories less than provided by many weight-reducing diets.

People not only need an adequate quantity of food each day; they must also have the right quality. This means having enough protein, vitamins, minerals, and trace nutrients. Serious protein malnutrition is as effective as near starvation in robbing human beings of their ability to function effectively and intelligently, and is most dangerous during the prenatal months, infancy, and childhood. During these periods, the body is developing, and the effects of malnutrition at any stages cannot be corrected later. Its victims will be handicapped for life. On February 10, 1966, in his message to Congress on the war on hunger, President Lyndon B. Johnson emphasized this point:

Beyond simple hunger there lies the problem of malnutrition. . . . Malnutrition saps a child's ability to learn. It weakens the nation's ability to progress. It can—and must—be attacked vigorously.

Today, in the developing nations, some 171 million children under 7 years of age and some 98 million between 7 and 14 suffer seriously from malnutrition, particularly protein malnutrition. The prospects for the millions to be born in the next 15 years are equally dismal—unless we reduce the pressure of population on food supply and upgrade the quality and quantity of what is available.

Most of the increase in food production must come from land already in cultivation. There is still some unused land suitable for agriculture, however—particularly in tropical South America and Africa. When I visited Brazil, I was impressed with its vast acreage of unused and underused land. In countries and regions where such fertile, well-watered land is unused, the area under cultivation can be expanded. However, to do so will require heavy investments, particularly by governments, to make the new lands attractive to settlers. Roads, markets, schools, and health facilities will have to be built. The assurance of land ownership, or other arrangements, will have to be provided to ensure a necessary degree of economic stability and promise to new farmers. Much of such potentially arable unused land also requires heavy investments to overcome soil and climatic problems. Water, temperature, and light are as important to agriculture as is land. We have only begun to learn how to carry on scientific agriculture in tropical areas and areas with very cold climates. This important form of agricultural development should be encouraged wherever practicable.

But, for most of the countries in the temperate zone, and

even for many of those in the tropics, the expansion of land area under cultivation is about over. To increase production these countries will have to learn to grow more food on available farmlands. They will have to take better advantage of science and technology.

Technology, the process that makes new use of old resources and brings new resources into being, enables man to improve upon nature—to make the unproductive productive and the productive more productive. The technological revolution in agriculture is relatively new and has taken place on a relatively small part of the world's farmlands. But its impact has been so great and its prospects so apparently limitless, that, for the first time in history, man can visualize a world without hunger. The development and spread of technology requires research, education in the broadest sense, and capital. I will discuss these in detail in later chapters.

Unfortunately, for the developing world as a whole, food production still presents a grim picture. Even though, since 1960, many nations have made notable increases in total production, on a per capita basis they have at best stood still. Nothing is left to meet the increased demands generated by improved incomes. When per capita income climbs from very low levels, 40 to 50 per cent of that increase is spent on food. The developing countries are on a food-population treadmill. They have had to increase production at a significant rate just to keep up with population growth, but they have made little, if any, progress in closing the food-people gap.

The economies of many of the developing countries are heavily dominated by agriculture. As much as 80 per cent of the population may rely on agriculture for its livelihood. If progress is made in agriculture, it buoys the whole economy; but if agriculture is stagnant, even spectacular gains in the industrial sector may help only a limited number of people. In a country that seeks economic development through industrialization alone, workers may be attracted to industry by higher wages, and the ratio of farm to nonfarm population may change. But industrial workers must eat. Unless the remaining farmers learn to produce more efficiently, food must be imported. Encouraging such one-sided development was a mistake made by both recipient and aid-giving nations during the 1950's. Neglect of agriculture has brought many developing countries to the point where they must import food to survive. Without question, they will have to import substantial amounts of food for some time to come.

Hunger and malnutrition are not new evils. But broad public knowledge of their scope and intensity is new. For the first time in history, the possibility exists that they can be eradicated. However, the effort is just beginning.

At this hour, we are in danger of losing the war on hunger. Society has the knowledge and the ability to bring population and food production into better alignment, but is failing, so far, to put forth enough effort to use what it knows. To tap the potential for increasing agricultural production and controlling population growth around the world will take continuing massive assistance from the developed countries. Even more important, it will take willingness on the part of the developing countries to commit themselves and a sufficient quantity of their own resources to utilize that assistance efficiently and effectively.

A World Role for American Agriculture

A friend of mine, a steel worker, is making payments on a new house and recently bought a color television set. He is considering trading in his old car for a new model. He works hard and earns every cent he gets, but he and millions of other people who have such things, have them because they live in one of the developed nations—for him, the United States. My friend spends less than $1 out of every $5 that he takes home for food, and 50 cents more covers his clothing needs. Housing takes about 75 cents. Thus, after providing for his necessities, he still has $2.75 out of every $5 that he can spend for such things as education, an automobile, and household conveniences.

If my friend were living in one of the poor, less developed nations, he would have to spend $3 out of every $5 that he earned for food—and he might earn only about $5 in a week. Housing and clothing would take practically all the rest of his money. For what he spent, he would get a smaller amount of food, often of poorer quality and less variety, than he would get for the same amount of money in the United States.

Development in the United States has taken a long time and much effort. Like many other nations, we have developed our natural resources by accumulating a body of knowledge and applying it to the solution of problems. The result of our developed technology is that today most American families have cars and live in houses with central heat, hot and cold running water, flush toilets, electric lights and refrigeration, radio, and television. We have as much food as we can eat, of the kind that we want to eat, and more clothes than we really need. Though we have not yet eliminated poverty from the United States, we have reached a stage of development where its elimination is a realistic national goal, to which I believe the American people are committed.

Perhaps if we were completely isolated from other countries, we might not find it essential to help their peoples obtain the basic necessities that we take for granted. No nation lives in isolation, however. For many years, through every means of communication, as private citizens or in government programs, we have been telling the world about "the American way of life." We have entered exhibits in trade fairs from Paris to Djakarta, giving people everywhere an opportunity to see the quality and quantity of our material possessions. We have exported our books, magazines, and newspapers, as well as our films and television shows, to innumerable distant cities. In increasing numbers, our statesmen, scientists, businessmen, and tourists travel all over the world, talking wherever they go, beckoning friends and potential friends: "Follow us and you too can have these good things." More than any other single nation, we have sparked the revolution of rising expectations, in which all the peoples of the world seek abundance for themselves.

If anyone were to ask me what is most responsible for this

revolution, I would say the transistor radio. Everywhere, in grass shacks and mud huts, people once completely cut off from industrialized society can be found with little transistor radios, hearing about a great world outside, where it sounds as if other people live much better. Naturally, these enchanted listeners aspire to the life about which they are learning. Furthermore, they usually want it not next year, next month, nor even tomorrow, but today.

The United States of America has been richly blessed. I believe it is only right that we share some of these blessings. Every great religion teaches that he who is blessed with much should share with those who have little. This precept is one by which most Americans seek to live. Most of us do try to follow the admonition to be our brother's keeper. In a spirit of simple goodness alone, it is right and proper that we share both our food and our knowledge with other countries that need them.

But there is another reason for us to share. If we, a nation of 200 million people in a world of 3.5 billion, fail now to do our utmost to help extend the benefits of a great society to all people, we can expect increasingly destructive famines, revolutions, and wars. The hungry man will hate; the hungry man will steal. The hungry mob will loot and pillage; the hungry nation will make war.

In the spring of 1966, in Montreal, former Defense Secretary Robert S. McNamara pointed out that over the preceding eight years serious outbreaks of violence had occurred far more frequently in the have-not nations than in the richer countries. He noted:

Since 1958 only one of these 27 [rich] nations has suffered a major internal upheaval on its own territory. Among the 38 very poor nations—those with a per capita income of under $100 a year—not less than 32 have suffered significant conflicts. Indeed, they have had an average of 2 major outbreaks of violence per country in the 8-year period. . . . What is worse, [these] have been predominantly conflicts of a prolonged nature. There is an irrefutable relationship between violence and economic backwardness. And the trend of such violence is up, not down. When people are hungry and poor, they look toward any promise of a better life.

The preservation of today's world and all of its people, including ourselves, depends upon sharing abundance and technical skills. It depends on supporting organizations for resolving conflicts between nations, for ensuring human rights, and for broadening the horizons of all peoples. We have only begun to struggle with these problems. The need is urgent, the lessons of history are indisputable.

LESSONS OF EARLIER YEARS

We in the United States are coming only slowly and painfully to realize that it is in our interest as a nation to make a long-range commitment to share our food and our knowledge. In the past, we have helped cheerfully and generously in emergencies brought on by natural disaster and war. These efforts bore little resemblance to the programs we embarked on after World War II, as we groped to devise a firm, long-range policy for assisting the developing nations to achieve economic growth. It may be worthwhile, however, to recall some of these early private and government programs in food aid.

In 1891–92, for instance, nationwide voluntary organizations sprang up almost overnight to handle contributions of grain and money for the relief of a famine in Russia. Jeremiah Rusk, Secretary of the Department of Agriculture, advised on the best methods for processing and shipping the relief donations, and even sent a corn specialist to St. Petersburg to advise on the preparation of food from corn meal, which had been contributed in ship-load quantities by the people of Illinois, Iowa, Nebraska, and other states.

During and after World War I, food supply and famine

relief programs became government operations for the first time. The American people were asked to observe wheatless Mondays and Wednesdays, meatless Tuesdays, and porkless Thursdays and Saturdays to conserve food for shipment to our allies. After the war ended, the President established the American Relief Administration to help the hungry people of devastated Europe. Between July, 1919, and June, 1920, total exports of food from the United States were 214 per cent of the average annual exports for the five years preceding the war.

Many years afterward, in July, 1963, I had a personal experience that demonstrated to me how important American food had been in making friends during and after World War I. Mrs. Freeman and I were on tour of the Soviet Union with a group of U.S. agricultural experts. We visited Orenburg in the "new lands" areas, where we inspected the gigantic 270,000-acre Adamovsky state wheat farm. We were met by I. L. Molchaninov, chairman of the Orenburg district Rural Executive Committee. The first words Mr. Molchaninov said to me, through a translator of course, when he greeted us at the airplane ramp, was that he remembered American food coming to Russia in 1921 to help fight the famine following World War I. Later, I learned that, like me, he was born in 1918. That made him only three years old when the food shipments arrived. But their impression on him had been indelible. During the next several days, he made reference to it on a number of occasions. Our generosity had had a very strong impact on this local leader. And what was true in his case is undoubtedly true of millions of people throughout the Soviet Union who ate American food in 1921. These people appreciated the generosity of America, and some today are also aware that it was free-enterprise, private-ownership agriculture that produced such abundance for the United States that it could share its food with others.

During the Great Depression of the 1930's and on into the early 1940's, the U.S. Department of Agriculture attempted food-supply management for the first time. New ways were devised for getting food to people who could not afford to buy enough of it. A domestic program to supply school children with hot lunches was begun. The "penny milk program" provided extra milk for children of low-income families. A food stamp plan, whereby low-income families could get more food and a greater variety of food for their food dollars was tried experimentally in selected cities. These schemes proved to be the forerunners for the National School Lunch Program and the Food Stamp Plan, which today are firmly established and reach about 20 million children and more than 2 million members of low-income families all over the United States.

Other Depression-born domestic programs to help farmers get back on their feet economically posed a more difficult problem. Prices received by farmers would not rise much as long as they produced more than people could buy. The federal government helped by paying farmers to reduce the production of certain crops, and by keeping part of the surplus off the market through loans to those who stored their crops in sealed bins and bonded warehouses. Thus began our controversial federal farm commodity programs. By 1940, the United States had enough wheat in storage to supply its recognized needs for two years, and enough corn to last for over a year.

It was fortunate that the United States had these large reserves of food at that time, for World War II had begun in Europe. The Germans nearly won the war in 1941, as much by destroying the stored food reserves of the British as by their military victories. American food helped save the British. The Lend-Lease Act of March 11, 1941, provided England and other allies with food, as well as guns and airplanes. Food purchasing for Lend-Lease was assigned to the Department of Agriculture, whose agencies had handled the school lunch, food stamp, and surplus storage programs. Their expertise was quickly put to new and broader use. The slogan adapted was "Food will win the war and write the peace." How much these words foreshadowed the tremendous part that food has played in writing and keeping the peace since World War II no one then guessed.

The experience of the Department of Agriculture in planning for more orderly production and marketing of food formed a solid foundation for dealing with the food-supply problems of the war years. Many improvements in food preservation had been developed. Quick freezing of meats, fish, vegetables, and fruits had become commercially practical, and frozen foods were on the market in some areas. A process for producing dry skim milk that could be reconstituted into fluid milk had reached commercial production. New low-temperature processes for extracting oil from peanuts, soybeans, and cottonseed produced a high-quality oil suitable for human food. Wartime needs greatly accelerated this type of research. Progress was made in developing food products high in nutritive value but small in bulk. Food packaging was greatly improved, so that humidity, rough handling, and extremes in temperatures would not result in spoilage.

The tremendous food needs of these years brought about the first real efforts to develop systematic estimates of food requirements, not only for the United States, but for the allied nations, the gradually enlarging occupied enemy territory, and even the neutral countries. In the United States, anticipated requirements were translated, insofar as practicable, into production goals. Programs were planned to encourage farmers to produce more of the needed foods, such as meat, milk, and oilseed crops.

There were mistakes made, of course. Some of the problems that emerged from these early efforts to plan production goals and to persuade farmers to make shifts in their usual farming patterns should give us sympathetic insights into the problems of developing nations. For example, in 1942, farmers were persuaded to plant a large acreage of peanuts, but many of them had not had previous experience with this crop, and the weather that year was not favorable for peanuts. Thus, the harvest was poor. Farmers lost money and became disillusioned. In subsequent years, despite official exhortation, peanut acreage fell short of the goals. Similarly, production goals for soybeans were set at a high level, and farmers planted large acreages. But, when the crop was harvested, it was discovered that there were very few mills in the Midwest to crush the seeds and extract the oil. Most of the crop had to be shipped to cottonseed crushing mills in the South. A crash program was started to build new crushing mills in the Midwest to handle future crops. Despite all the problems encountered, however, the food-supply lines were kept full during those war years. Although many people went hungry, especially in the occupied areas, there was no widespread starvation.

The wartime efforts to fulfill food requirements provided a powerful stimulus to the science of nutrition. Before World War II, home economists in the Department of Agriculture had translated minimum nutritional requirements into individual and family diets on four cost levels. These were used as standards for developing estimates of food requirements, both here and abroad. Since there were not enough of the vitamin-rich foods to meet minimum requirements, some foods, such as bread, which formed a large part of the diet of millions of Europeans and Americans, were enriched with minerals and vitamins. Fortunately, the chemists were able to develop inexpensive processes for manufacturing synthetic vitamins.

CHANGES AFTER WORLD WAR II

After the war ended, the United States became engaged in the greatest relief operation to avert famine in history. Two years later, food production in Europe had still not returned to prewar levels, and appeared to have reached a plateau. There was not enough food for an adequate diet for millions of industrial workers, nor was there enough foreign exchange to buy food in the world market. Only continued large-scale donations of food by the United States could avert continued widespread undernourishment and malnutrition. Meanwhile, political unrest was increasing all over Europe.

But the American public was showing signs of growing impatience with foreign aid. Price controls had been relaxed and then abandoned. Inflation had set in. People resented the increased price of food and blamed it on aid programs. They raised serious questions about the drain on our natural resources resulting from foreign aid. In answer, President Harry S. Truman set up several top-level committees to analyze the problem and make recommendations. The conclusions of these study groups were: (1) The U.S. economy could support a greatly expanded aid program if economic growth were not stifled by inflation; (2) in Europe, wartime destruction combined with postwar occupation policies and long-term malnutrition had created an economic situation that made quick recovery to prewar levels impossible without outside help; and (3) the United States could not afford to let Europe stagnate.

THE MARSHALL PLAN

In an address before a joint session of the Senate and the House of Representatives on November 17, 1947, the President recommended: (1) economic and military aid for certain Western European countries to enable them to resist the spread of Communism, and (2) a program to curb inflation in the United States. The resulting foreign-aid program was called the European Recovery Program—or, more familiarly, the Marshall Plan, for General George C. Marshall, who, as Secretary of State, had propounded the basic idea in a commencement address at Harvard earlier that year.

The Marshall Plan went into effect June 30, 1952. It cost over $12.5 billion and enabled the Europeans to restore the means of production in agriculture and industry and to become a living force in promoting the economic well-being of the world. What made the Marshall Plan unprecedented was not only its scope and its success, but the principles upon which it was based. It made American help conditional upon self-help by the European countries.

During the first two years, we shipped large quantities of food abroad, which helped to restore the vigor of the working population. This food was paid for in the local currency of the recipient countries and the funds were deposited in special accounts, to be used in programs mutually agreed upon by the United States and each recipient country. We sent livestock, seed, fertilizer, and farm machinery, together with experts in such fields as agricultural education, marketing, and food processing. By the end of the Marshall Plan, both agricultural and industrial production were well above prewar levels, and a solid base had been laid for continued economic growth.

POINT FOUR PROGRAM

The United States, in the meantime, had moved into a period of increasing productivity and prosperity. But other parts of the world were not faring so well. Famine threatened India and Pakistan in 1952. Civil war in China disrupted production and produced hunger. The Arab countries of the Near East were swamped with refugees from Israel. In his inaugural address on January 20, 1949, President Truman proposed the Point Four program. He said, in part:

We must embark on a bold new program for making the benefits of our scientific advances and industrial progress available for the improvement and growth of underdeveloped areas. . . .

For the first time in history humanity possesses the knowledge and the skill to relieve the suffering of these people.

We invite other countries to pool their technological resources in this undertaking. . . .

All countries, including our own, will greatly benefit from a constructive program for the better use of the world's human and natural resources. Experience shows that our commerce with other countries expands as they progress industrially and economically.

Greater production is the key to prosperity and peace. And the key to greater production is a wider and more vigorous application of modern scientific and technical knowledge.

Only by helping the least fortunate of its members to help themselves can the human family achieve the decent, satisfying life that is the right of all people.

These inspiring ideas, as valid today as when they were uttered, were part of a fresh, bold concept. It was the first direct, unqualified expression of broad American concern for the welfare of the newly developing nations. It proposed to help them for their own sakes and for the sake of humanity.

The Point Four program, as first established, was based upon the assumption that relatively inexpensive exports of American technology would act as catalytic agents in transforming developing economies. Technology, it was assumed, could simply be transferred to another part of the world with little research and experimentation to adapt it to entirely different physical and economic conditions. This oversimplified view obscured the fact that many nations needed large investments of capital. And many technicians overlooked the importance of agriculture to sound economic development. Nevertheless, a start had been made.

Point Four lost some of its thrust after the Korean War. Emphasis on technical assistance and agricultural development gave way to emphasis on industrialization and heavy capital investments for such needs as roads and power plants. The principle of self-help got lost in the shuffle.

By this time, surpluses of food were again beginning to accumulate in the United States. The world-wide need for more food was both real and compelling, but there was no effective machinery for the transfer of food from rich countries with booming agriculture to poor countries where food production was inadequate to meet needs. International food programs began to be labeled dumping schemes. Selling food cheaply or giving food away, it was said, depressed prices, discouraged production, and destroyed producers in the less developed countries. These were troublesome charges. Could it be true that by making relief food available we were reducing, rather than encouraging, total world food production?

We went to work trying to determine how the dilemma could be resolved. How could we use the food that we produced beyond our own needs at home to prevent hunger and starvation around the world without adversely affecting food production in other countries? We found the answer in the principle of "additionality," by which we would give or sell on easy terms our surplus food to needy countries, provided they would agree that this food would be in addition to the food that they regularly bought through commercial channels.

PUBLIC LAW 480

This idea was embodied in the Agricultural Trade Development and Assistance Act of 1954 (Public Law 480), which authorized the donation of food to international relief organizations and the sale of food for the currency of the receiving country, rather than for U.S. dollars. The so-called soft currency would then be spent in the country of origin. Some of this money could be used by the United States to pay expenses in the country for such purposes as maintaining our embassy, but the bulk of it was to be loaned or given to the country for development projects. Thus, it could be used to pay laborers for building dams, roads, or schools. P.L. 480 was later amended to provide also for the sale of food at world prices for U.S. dollars, both on long-term and short-term credit.

From 1954 to 1961, the volume of food shipped to other countries grew steadily. During this period, the primary emphasis was on getting rid of surplus foods that were piling up in the United States, rather than on economic development in the receiving countries. Certainly there was a strong humanitarian motivation in making food available to hundreds of millions of people around the world; however, the law required that only commodities then in surplus could be shipped. As a result, when U.S. stocks were reduced to reasonable levels, the offer to give or sell such products under P.L. 480 was withdrawn. This was the case periodically with such items as butter, dry skim milk, cheese, and vegetable oils. Wheat continued in surplus, and generous quantities of wheat were made available around the world.

Originally, P.L. 480 contained a legal framework for international transfers of food to deficit countries. But the primary emphasis was on getting rid of surpluses. Assistance for hungry people and economic development were secondary.

EXTENSIONS AND EXPANSION OF P.L. 480

In 1961, the basic attitude toward P.L. 480 and the use of food aid changed sharply. President John F. Kennedy said, on January 24 of that year:

American agricultural abundance offers a great opportunity for the United States to promote the interests of peace in a significant way and to play an important role in helping to provide a more adequate diet for peoples all around the world. We must make the most vigorous and constructive use possible of this opportunity. We must narrow the gap between abundance here at home and near starvation abroad. Humanity and prudence, alike, counsel a major effort on our part.

On March 16, he told Congress:

We have barely begun to explore the ways in which our abundance can advance the cause of peace and freedom around the world, and contribute to the well-being and stability of undeveloped nations, whose peoples eye our storage stockpiles with hungry dissatisfaction. I have already dispatched a series of missions to such areas to ascertain how we can best use our food in a helpful fashion. In addition, I ask the Congress . . . to extend and expand the Agricultural Trade Development and Assistance Act of 1954 [P.L. 480]. . . . Unless there is some assurance of a continuing program we can neither make the advance plans best suited to an effective instrument of foreign policy nor gauge its long-term effect upon our domestic programs. Title I sales should be authorized at a higher level; and our contributions of food and fiber to voluntary agencies such as CARE for use abroad should be liberalized.

Congress acted favorably. It extended and expanded P.L. 480 to assure a continuing food-assistance program.

Again, in 1964 and 1965, President Johnson urged extension and additional strengthening of P.L. 480. Both years, Congress extended and amended portions of the act. The authorization for donations of food for economic development was increased from $300 million to $400 million annually. Voluntary agencies were encouraged to conduct food-for-work programs using donated food. The use of foreign currencies from the sale of food to pay the currency costs of food-for-work and school lunch programs was authorized. Approximately $2.5 million in AID funds was appropriated to fortify nonfat dry milk with vitamins A and D, to fortify U.S.-processed flour and corn meal with calcium, and to pay the cost of adding vitamins and minerals to blended foods made from grains, oilseeds, and milk. The Secretary of Agriculture was authorized to purchase dairy

products at market prices for use in child feeding and in domestic and foreign relief programs when the government did
not have these products in storage in sufficient quantity to
meet needs.

The Secretary of Agriculture has important responsibilities
in carrying forward P.L. 480. Shortly after assuming office on
January 26, 1961, I set down the principles that I have tried
to follow throughout my service as Secretary:

We must expand our programs to utilize our agricultural abundance as an instrument to encourage economic growth in underdeveloped areas of the world, as one of our greatest weapons for
peace and freedom, and thus a source of strength for our nation
and of security for our people.

ACHIEVEMENTS UNDER TITLE I OF P.L. 480

The largest volume of P.L. 480 shipments has been under
Title I, with payments made in the currency of the receiving
country. Funds are deposited to the credit of the United States
and are used in accordance with agreements negotiated between the United States and each participating country. The
lion's share of these funds is returned to the receiving countries in the form of loans or grants for economic development.
From the beginning of the program until September 30, 1960,
the equivalent, in local currency, of $885.2 million had been
loaned and $79 million had been disbursed in grants for
economic development. Since 1960, we have greatly accelerated the effort to put these local currencies to work for economic development—$2,555 million has been loaned and
$1,426 million has been granted.

The largest local currency program in Latin America is in
Brazil. Although the southern part of Brazil is progressive and
developing rapidly, there is a large region known as the
Northeast, where poverty and economic stagnation have prevailed for at least a half-century. Transportation, communica-

tion, education, and health facilities are inadequate. In many ways, the Northeast may be likened to our own Appalachian highland area.

Part of this Brazilian area once enjoyed prosperity from extensive mining operations, but these have closed down, and the stranded people gain a meager subsistence from farming the poor soils. Much of the area is plagued by recurring droughts. A concentrated regional program in the nine states of the Northeast, financed in part with funds from P.L. 480 sales, seeks to develop a livestock economy and to provide education, health, transportation, and public utilities in an effort to enable these people to contribute to the economic development of their country.

Achievements in East Pakistan in the last several years, financed largely by P.L. 480–generated rupees, are perhaps the most impressive to be found anywhere in the developing world. The program there combines local democratic self-government with a government-financed but locally planned and executed public works program. Two of its stated purposes are: (1) to provide employment for large numbers of landless agricultural workers who are normally without work and go hungry during the winter dry season, and (2) to construct badly needed farm-to-market roads, irrigation ditches, flood embankments, and small-scale drainage ditches. This works program is available to the villagers only if they themselves develop acceptable plans and meet established standards of performance. The land for the works projects must be donated by the villagers. Since the equivalent of 3 acres of land is needed for each mile of road, flood embankment, or irrigation ditch and since the average farm is only 3.4 acres, the farmers obviously must be fully committed to the program or they would not band together to donate the necessary land.

Over 70,000 miles of farm-to-market roads have been built. Today, East Pakistan is one of the few places in the developing world where all of the farmers can get their produce to market. These roads have reduced the cost of transport from $1.50 per ton-mile to 50 cents per ton-mile, and the means of transport has shifted—from people's heads to bicycles and rickshaws. About 4 million acres (15 per cent) of the cultivated land has been improved. Rice production has increased more than 2 million tons, or 25 per cent. Crop diversification and production for market is increasing. Hundreds of thousands of subsistence farmers are entering a modern market economy for the first time.

American food can make a great contribution to efforts of this kind. On October 14, 1961, while visiting Pakistan, I signed an agreement for the second largest P.L. 480 program up to that date. Over a four-year period, Pakistan purchased $622 million worth of wheat, feed grains, vegetable oil, and other commodities, and paid for them with rupees. Some 70 per cent of these rupees were loaned or granted to the Government of Pakistan to finance economic development projects. A portion of these rupees was used to pay for village labor on work projects. In all probability, the workers used their wages to buy some of the U.S. food.

Since 1961, I have participated in many signing ceremonies for P.L. 480 agreements. None has meant more to me personally than the 1961 agreement with Pakistan. Following the signing ceremony in Karachi, we visited a village near the Khyber Pass. There I had one of the most gratifying experiences of the seven years that I have served as Secretary of Agriculture. We were received most hospitably by the leading citizens of the village of Gangu Bahadur. Most of them were older men, but the newly elected mayor, Malik Mohammed Shaffi, was a young man, proud of his village and determined to improve it. This was during the very early days of President Ayub Khan's guided democracy and the election in which Shaffi became mayor, or chairman of the village's Union Council, was the first under the new regime. After we had toured the tiny village, the mayor took me to a little enclosure, prepared with carpets, where we sat and had refreshments. He described to me his hopes to build a better village. In the course of the conversation, I asked him what his village needed most.

He responded promptly, "A school."

I asked him what he was doing about getting one. He looked at me somewhat sadly and said they had filed an application with the central government, but had not yet heard.

"We have so little resources here," he said almost apologetically.

"If you had wheat," I asked him, "which you could use as wages for the men of this village who have nothing to do when they are not working in their fields, could you build a school?"

"Yes," he replied promptly, "we certainly could."

I guess I had caught some of his enthusiasm, for my response was, "All right, you'll get some wheat, and some day I hope I can see that school."

We made our farewells and went on our way. Later, I talked with our agricultural attaché, Donald MacDonald, and asked him to see if an arrangement could be worked out to make wheat available to this village to help pay for labor if the village provided the materials to build a school. Ivan C. Packard, the Pakistan country director of Wheat Associates, Inc., a trade organization that cooperates closely with the U.S. Department of Agriculture in foreign-market development, personally pitched in and saw the job through.

Almost two years later, the Pakistani ambassador called my office in Washington and asked for an appointment. I had no idea what he wanted. When he came in, he asked me if I remembered my trip to the village near the Khyber Pass. I told him that of course I did.

"Well," he said, "that school you talked about has been

built, and it was dedicated just last month to the United States Secretary of Agriculture."

Then he showed me a picture. An inscription on the front of the whitewashed building said, "Dedicated to Orville L. Freeman, United States Secretary of Agriculture." The ambassador went on to tell me that approximately 1,000 bushels of U.S. wheat had been released from Pakistani Government storage to help pay labor costs. The villagers donated the funds for building materials, and their contributions were augmented by a Government of Pakistan grant. The school accommodates 100 children, from six different villages.

The Pakistani ambassador smiled and said, "If you want to run for public office, that's where you should go. Everyone in the entire area will vote for you for anything you might stand for."

Under Title I of P.L. 480, foreign currencies may also be loaned to U.S. or foreign private businesses, including co-operatives, for improving the processing and marketing facilities for agricultural products. From the time that this program was initiated in 1957 until the end of 1966, 397 loans were made to private firms in twenty-five countries in an amount equivalent to $341.3 million.

About 20 per cent of the total amount of foreign currencies accruing from sales under Title I agreements are reserved for the use of the United States. These funds pay part of the expenses of our embassies, military forces, U.S. Information Agency programs, and trade development programs aimed at increasing exports to countries that can pay for them. These foreign currencies also finance educational and cultural exchange programs, as well as grants for research—all of which help substantially with our balance of payments, since they enable us to pay our expenses without exporting U.S. dollars.

Research supported with P.L. 480 funds must be potentially beneficial to the United States, as well as to the country in which the work is done. Some of these research projects are very interesting. For example, research is now under way in Uruguay to find a biological control method for the fire ant. Success in this research would be useful to many farmers in the southern United States, where one species of fire ant also is a destructive pest. Uruguayan scientists have found a parasitic ant that lives as a kind of guest in the earth mounds built by the fire ant. Oddly, fire ants neglect their own kind to give the parasitic ants food, space, and care, thereby reducing the vigor of their own colonies. Some day the United States may import the parasitic ants from Uruguay—but not until we are sure that they will damage nothing but fire ants.

The medical and health research programs in foreign countries, financed by our food shipments under P.L. 480, include attacks on some troublesome diseases. One is schistosomiasis —a disease caused by a worm that infests the blood stream of man and attacks the intestines, bladder, liver, and spleen. A snail that lives in irrigation ditches acts as host to the schistosomes during one stage of their life cycle, and the incidence of the disease has been increasing in many countries as irrigation has been extended. Research on schistosomiasis is being financed through a grant of P.L. 480 local currency in Brazil.

Experimental programs for rehabilitating people handicapped by blindness, arthritis, and other disabilities are making notable contributions. Methods of teaching blind persons to operate textile-mill machinery and data-processing equipment, as well as handicraft and agricultural tools, are being studied in India, Israel, Syria, and the United Arab Republic.

Food Donations Under Titles II and III of P.L. 480

Title II of the new P.L. 480 (Titles II and III before the 1966 extension) authorizes donations of food for foreign use. The Agency for International Development administers donation programs conducted by voluntary agencies, intergovernmental organizations, and friendly governments.

U.S. food is available for disaster relief whenever and wherever it is needed and is also available on a sustained basis for the feeding of refugees. But, although they do much good, direct emergency feeding programs are only stop-gap measures. Since 1961, we have sought to make more constructive use of food donated under Title II.

One way of building for tomorrow is to ensure the health and vitality of today's children. To this end, we have greatly expanded our donations for school lunch programs in developing countries. In one year, 1964, the number of children in Latin America receiving school lunches from U.S. food increased from 10 million to 14 million. Because each lunch program is carefully planned, approved, and supervised to meet U.S. Government regulations and accepted practices, the increase in such a short time was a tremendous accomplishment. We have also sought to improve the nutrition of preschool children and of pregnant and nursing mothers. Studies have shown that the most seriously malnourished segment of the population in poor countries is usually that of children between weaning and school age. We are emphasizing the use of vitamin-, mineral-, and protein-enriched foods for these children. AID funds are being used for facilities needed for child-feeding programs. This does not mean the installation of modern cafeterias, but, rather, the building and equipping of simple, clean facilities where food can be processed and distributed in a sanitary manner, even if the lunchroom is only a shed roofed with palm leaves, and the lunch only a bun made from enriched flour and served with a cup of reconstituted enriched, dry skim milk. (This is not to say that more substantial facilities do not exist in many places. One new school lunch cafeteria in Bogota, Colombia, dedicated in my honor, compares favorably with anything in the United States. Its equipment was donated by American industry.)

In a growing number of countries, there is a calculated shift from the use of donated food for relief feeding to its use in food-for-work community development programs. Donated food may also be sold, with the proceeds to be used to pay part of the workers' wages in cash. In addition, the 1964 amendments to P.L. 480 authorized the use of foreign currencies accumulated under Title I sales to pay part of the wages of laborers on community development projects. About 14 million people benefited from these self-help projects in 1966.

Self-help, food-for-work activities in 1966 involved 43,800 volunteer workers in the Philippines. Here, U.S. voluntary agencies worked with the Philippine National Economic Council and the AID mission in a program that drew into active participation village captains, municipal mayors, provincial governors, lay leaders, teachers, priests, and pastors in 46 provinces. Some 638 self-help projects have been completed, with 141 continuing. They involved construction or repair of 429 classrooms, 45 dams, 400 kilometers of irrigation canals, 390 kilometers of feeder roads, 167 kilometers of foot trails between villages in mountainous regions, and hundreds of water-sealed toilets. Also included were reforestation of 247 acres of land, clearing and cultivation of 7,111 acres of land for farming, and numerous community-action programs.

While most of our programs are bilateral—nation to nation —U.S. food donations under P.L. 480 are helping the World Food Program. This program was established by the United Nations and the Food and Agriculture Organization, at the instance of the United States in 1963, to meet special needs and to discover how food aid could be used on a multilateral basis in the developing countries to stimulate economic and social development. It is too early yet to judge how effective multinational food aid will be, but so far the World Food Program shows promise.

TODAY'S DOLLAR CUSTOMERS

To those who complain that foreign aid is a never-ending procedure and that we are giving away too much, we can say that many of yesterday's P.L. 480 foreign-currency customers have become today's dollar customers. Title IV, added to P.L. 480 in 1959, provides for long-term deliveries of up to ten years and repayment periods of up to twenty years for agricultural exports to be paid for in dollars. Programs under this title help to ease the transition for countries moving up the economic ladder—from recipients of foreign aid to full trading partners.

During the late 1950's, Spain obtained most of its agricultural imports under Title I of Public Law 480, paying with pesetas rather than dollars. Since 1961–62, Spain has shifted to commercial purchasing of farm products and is now one of our ten best dollar customers. Greece, Israel, and Japan, are other examples of countries where aid has been replaced by trade.

Japan today is our largest market for American farm products. In 1963, the Japanese Minister of Agriculture told a meeting of the American Food for Peace Council that U.S. food shipments after World War II had brought his country back from the brink of mass starvation, put a brake on inflation, and paved the way for reconstruction of Japanese industry. American food, he said, had brought about a revolution in eating habits for his countrymen. They now eat twice as much wheat, oil, and fats, and four times as much meat, and drink three times as much milk as they did before World War II. Because of their improved diet, Japanese school children are now an average of 4 inches taller than before the war, and the Japanese are having to replace school desks that are too small for the present generation of pupils.

PORTENTS OF CHANGE

As we look to the future, it is clear that only in the developing nations, with their billions of people, will the United States find markets to utilize its great and growing productive capacity. We continue to compete strongly for markets in Western Europe and in other developed countries, but the agriculture in these lands is expanding rapidly. Their population grows only moderately, and is already relatively well fed. Their demand for food increases at a much slower pace than in the developing world, where people need and demand more food and will buy it as soon as they have the money to do so.

Our use of food for economic development has been unique in the history of man. Because it had no precedent, it has entailed a learning process for us and for the rest of the world. In 1961, we had been providing food aid to people in hungry nations for many years, but were we helping them to become less hungry? No one really knew. How effective were our technical assistance and economic aid programs? Reports from some countries were buried in the files, but there was no over-all evaluation.

In the seven years that I have served as Secretary of Agriculture, we have been making a determined effort to learn more about the nature and magnitude of world food problems. At first, I was appalled at the gaps in our knowledge. We knew how much food was shipped in world trade, we knew our own production and that of other developed countries, but our data on production and consumption in most of Asia, Africa, and Latin America were negligible. I immediately began mobilizing the resources of the Department of Agriculture to gather and analyze data on current and future world food availability and needs, on the performance of countries that we had been trying to help with food and economic aid, and on the kinds of programs that would be effective in increasing world food production to meet man's needs. The Agency for International Development cooperated, and gave financial support. The United Nations' Food and Agriculture Organization, our own Budget Bureau, and other public and private agencies have also cooperated.

These studies revealed the data presented in Chapter 1. A later study, "Changes in Agriculture in 26 Developing Nations, 1948–1963," showed that some of these countries were increasing their agricultural production at rates far higher than any ever achieved by the highly developed nations, including the United States.

This record gives encouragement that agriculture can be sharply improved in the developing countries. It demonstrates what can be done under a variety of natural, political, social, religious, and economic conditions. Some of the countries studied are tropical, some are semitropical, and some lie in temperate climatic zones. They differ greatly in their rural population densities and in their potential for expanded cultivated area. They exhibit notable differences in the level and stage of economic development and in cultural characteristics. Some among the twenty-six studied have had much lower per capita incomes and levels of literacy, and less adequate educational systems than others that have improved their agriculture very little despite apparent advantages.

The key to success appears to be national understanding and will—an understanding of the importance of agriculture, and a determination to adopt policies and programs that make the most of favorable conditions, or circumvent or alter unfavorable ones. Geography, economic and social conditions, land, labor, and capital are all important, but by themselves they do not determine a nation's growth, either in agriculture or in general economic development. It is the responses and adaptations to those conditions—the policies and programs followed—that determine progress. In other words, the most important ingredient is what a winning football coach said explained his team's victory: desire.

But not all—not even many—of the hungry nations of the world are improving their agriculture fast enough. Another study, completed in 1967, showed that, in the developing countries importing U.S. grain, the percentage imported under P.L. 480 increased from one-third of total imports in 1959–61 to more than one-half in 1964–65. Clearly, food aid was not solving the world food problem. We were not helping enough people to feed themselves. The trends were in the wrong direction.

All of our assessments and all of our projections pointed to the imperative need already described in these pages: greatly accelerated food production in the hungry nations themselves. Our studies have convinced me that these nations can feed themselves in the next decade or two. But to do so will require vigorous action beginning right now, on a sustained basis, with the necessary resources of people and capital. In carrying forward such a program, social and economic studies are fully as important as scientific studies of plants, animals, and soils. Both kinds are essential. But only recently have we come to realize the importance of quickly learning more about what kinds of policies and programs make for greater success under specific conditions in a particular country.

President Johnson has recognized that renewed emphasis on self-help is the only way, in the long run, to promote the effort necessary if all of the people in the world are ever to get enough to eat. His war on hunger message to Congress on February 10, 1966, was a ringing call to action. The self-help program that he stressed in his recommendations provides for technical and capital assistance, as well as food aid for nations determined to help themselves. It was vigorously supported by both houses of Congress—and by members of both major political parties. It has received widespread public support in the United States and around the world.

Self-help is now a firmly established principle in U.S. food aid to foreign countries. I am confident that this country will always respond to emergencies, but our long-range sustained assistance will go in the future to those countries that resolve and demonstrate that they want to become self-supporting.

The authorizations for technical assistance to agriculture in the 1966 amendments to P.L. 480 are broader than those of any previous legislation. Research programs on tropical and subtropical agriculture are specifically authorized. The recruiting and training of agricultural experts for work in developing countries is also provided for in the law, reflecting congressional recognition that more technical assistance will require more U.S. citizens to participate in this world-wide effort. Today, we are short of experts. We have not been training enough of our youth in agricultural fields. Since we have fewer farms and fewer opportunities for young people to go into farming, enrollments in our agricultural colleges have been declining. However, the Peace Corps has amply demonstrated that people who are not highly trained can make valuable contributions in education, community development, and small-scale farming. Strong efforts must be made to alert and convince potential professional agriculturists that a life of challenge and service awaits those who help the hungry nations to learn to feed themselves.

Another change in the food-aid picture is the elimination of the heavy surpluses of food in the United States—the result of misguided policies in the 1950's. Then we were prepared to give away surplus food almost on request. In the future, food to be used for aid will have to be planned and produced for that purpose. In the process, American producers must receive better prices. Otherwise, we risk "killing the hen that lays the golden egg."

The new authorizations under P.L. 480 and the Food and Agriculture Act of 1965 provide us with the authority to operate what is, in effect, a national food budget. We must avoid serious overproduction, not only to protect our own farmers but to avoid precipitous drops in world prices. Such falling prices can only undermine incentives for struggling producers in hungry countries just learning to use purchased seed, fertilizer, and insecticides. This budgeting of our food production won't be easy. It will take skill, determination, and the cooperation of many people. But I am firmly convinced that it can be done.

Continuing study and evaluation indicate that we are on the right course. As we accumulate more knowledge and experience, we can make increasingly sophisticated judgments. The President's Science Advisory Committee report, "The World Food Problem," of May, 1967, concluded that "gigantic efforts will be necessary in the developing countries to attain the desired food and income levels," and warned that the developed world "will have to assist in the next 20 years by providing a high level of economic and food assistance, private capital, and, perhaps even more important, creating an environment more favorable to the growth of exports from developing countries."

A more recent report, "The World Food Situation," published August 1, 1967, by the Department of Agriculture, looks to 1970, and then considers prospects likely to prevail up to 1980 under four different assumptions regarding rate of growth and development in hungry countries as well as in the productive capacity of the rich countries. Under any of the assumptions, according to the report, the world as a whole, in 1980, will have a capacity to produce more than enough grain to meet the world-wide demand for food.

This statement is of the utmost significance for the war on hunger. It has been misconstrued by many persons, including a number of newspaper headline writers, to mean that the war on hunger is not as crucial as has been claimed. Some even misinterpreted the statement to mean that the war on hunger had been won.

This is not the case. On the contrary, this statement indicates only that, as a world, we can produce enough food, at least until 1980, for everybody. It does not say that we can get the food to the 2 billion or more hungry stomachs that need it.

The full report goes on to say that the problem of hunger in the world cannot be separated from the economic gap between the 900 million inhabitants of the rich nations and the 2.5 billion who live in the poor nations. It says that we cannot win the war on hunger on the fertile fields of mid-America, but that these fields can contribute by buying time while we mobilize and march on the broad front of the developing countries themselves, which is where this war must be won.

It says, and I quote from the study:

The world food problem is basically one of disparity of food production and food availability between the developing and developed nations. It is inseparable from the development gap between rich and poor nations.

There is our task: to help alter social structures thousands of years in the making and customs that have more force than law and to put blood into economic systems that today are not able to sustain full life for more than 2 billion people.

Fortunately, since World War II we have learned and demonstrated that material well-being does not come in a fixed quantity, which, like a pie, can be divided into more pieces only by making each piece smaller. Instead, we have been busily engaged in baking a bigger pie. Perhaps it would be risky to say that the limit on productivity is infinite. Research and technology are constantly expanding our vistas. By sharing the fruits of our knowledge, we can share our abundance without diminishing our own plenty.

Difficulties of
Agricultural Development

Agriculture is the key to economic development. No country has developed a strong economy and a high standard of living without a highly productive agricultural sector. Yet, making agriculture more productive is the most difficult economic task that a nation can face.

Unfortunately, both the importance and difficulties of agricultural development are only now beginning to be appreciated in the developing countries and in those trying to help them. Because it seemed obvious that, as nations industrialized, agriculture employed a decreasing proportion of the labor force and produced a smaller proportion of the nation's goods, and that countries remaining primarily agricultural remained poor, while the industrial nations became rich, agricultural development was downgraded by planners everywhere. Efforts in the last twenty-five years to promote economic development based largely on industrialization have

46

exposed the fallacy of this view. Without agricultural development, general economic development soon bogs down in
problems of inflation, unemployment, and scarcities.

The emergence of such problems in country after country
has led us to re-examine our basic theories. We have come to
realize that all of today's advanced nations, even those like
the United Kingdom and Japan, which rely heavily upon imported supplies of agricultural products, moved from subsistence agriculture to commercial agriculture in the earlier
stages of their development.

In the developing countries, where per capita incomes
average $250 or less a year, agriculture typically accounts for
60–70 per cent of total employment and for 40–50 per cent of
the total income. This distribution of employment and total
income is similar to conditions that prevailed in the United
States, Canada, Australia, and the Western European countries about 150 years ago, and more recently in Japan, Israel,
and other rapidly developing countries.

Why is rapid agricultural development so important for
achieving successful total economic development? An adequate answer to this question calls for an explanation of the
role of agriculture in the total economic system. Let me first
consider it in the context of our experience in the United
States. From this experience, many parallels can be drawn
with situations in the developing nations of the world.

Agricultural develop goes hand & hand w/ economic

RELEVANCE OF THE U.S. EXPERIENCE *development; economic effects Conditions of country effects agriculture*

Five specific contributions of agriculture to total economic
development in the United States are particularly relevant to
the situation in most developing countries. These are not
mutually exclusive, nor were all of these contributions made
during the same periods in the history of the United States.

Increased Food Supplies. American agriculture supplied an
abundance of food, which helped set in motion and sustain

the whole process of economic development. Rapid advances in agricultural productivity have meant increased food supplies at relatively low prices. As a result, families have needed progressively less of their incomes to purchase food, and more has been available to spend for other things. At the beginning of the twentieth century, Americans spent about 40 per cent of their income for food. By 1967, they were spending only 17.7 per cent. This large drop in the share of income spent for food created an important market stimulus for expanding nonagricultural production. Abundant food supplies at relatively low prices meant improved real income for workers, less pressure to raise wages, and increased profitability for business and industry.

This sequence is particularly important for many of the developing countries now approaching a "take-off" phase in their economic development. Typically, these countries have quickly increasing populations and a rapidly growing demand for food. Unless domestic agricultural production expands rapidly, rising food prices will consume such a large proportion of workers' incomes that little will be left to spend for the products of industry.

In subsistence agriculture, farmers and their families consume the bulk of their own production. Most of the food they produce goes to feed the family; only a small part of the total enters market channels. The typical subsistence farmer is poor. When opportunity arises, he is likely to increase his own food consumption. Thus, when these farmers increase their food production, they usually consume most of the increase, and not much of it reaches the market. In commercial agriculture, little or none of the product is retained on the farm.

There are wide differences in productivity within agriculture in the developing countries. Many have well-developed, market-oriented production for some crops, especially those exported, and fairly high productivity levels. But the bulk of the farm production in these countries is carried out under primitive methods, largely for subsistence purposes, with relatively low yields.

When I was in Brazil in the summer of 1966, I saw many coffee plantations where the most up-to-date farming techniques were in use, and yields were high. In the same region, however, corn and rice yields were about one-third of those in the United States. Cattle were kept forty-eight months before being marketed, as contrasted with twenty-one months in the United States. Only 40–50 per cent of the cows calved annually, whereas in the United States 90–95 per cent of the cows have a calf each year. Such low levels of productivity have made it necessary for Brazil to import large amounts of food in the last few years for her rapidly growing urban population. Many developing nations have had similar experiences. The plain fact is that subsistence agriculture cannot sustain a growing economy.

Labor for Industry. Industrial development requires a steadily expanding labor force. Most developing countries have a surplus of labor in agriculture that can be attracted into expanding industries. But when rural people move into city jobs, they consume as much food as before. Unless the remaining farmers produce more efficiently, a labor shortage in agriculture soon develops, and the flow of labor into industry may be stopped, or reversed. Food prices rise under such circumstances, and inflation halts economic progress.

To illustrate, the Soviet Union, with all its industrialization, must still use about 35 per cent of its total work force in agriculture, while the United States uses only 5.2 per cent. Most of the developing countries employ more than 50 per cent of their total working force in agriculture. Clearly, if economic development is to take place, agriculture must become increasingly productive to provide food for the increasing nonfarm population.

Capital Accumulation. In today's developing countries,

large capital investments are needed. Roads, power plants, schools, irrigation, and other facilities are essential if agriculture is to increase its productivity. As farm output improves, the increased income will be invested largely in agricultural improvements and in the products of industry.

In the nineteenth century, Japan forced the transfer of capital from agriculture to industry through taxation. A good many developing countries have tried this technique, through heavy taxation of agricultural exports. In today's highly competitive world market, however, such taxation tends to have the effect of losing markets through overpricing, or bankrupting agriculture by depressing domestic prices below the cost of production.

In the last century in the United States, farmers' savings helped to finance industrial development. Similar investment does not seem likely in most of today's developing nations however. Probably the most valuable contribution that agriculture can make in the present state of development of many countries is in providing adequate food supplies at reasonable prices and in transferring human capital from agriculture to industry.

Agricultural Exports. Most developing countries earn a major portion of their foreign exchange by exporting agricultural products. Proceeds from the exports can be used to buy capital and consumer goods for both industry and agriculture or to pay off loans made by foreign investors.

If world demand for the agricultural exports of today's developing nations were expanding, as was world demand for American agricultural exports during the nineteenth century, such exports would be a valuable source of capital for development in those nations. Unfortunately, this has not been the case. Some of these agricultural exports, such as cotton, other fibers, and rubber, face strong competition from synthetics. The demand for others, such as coffee and cocoa, will increase only as the incomes of the poorer people, who live mostly in the exporting countries, increase.

Many developing countries have expanded production of agricultural products for export at the expense of needed domestic food production. This robbing Peter to pay Paul results in no net benefit to the country. The foreign exchange earned from agricultural exports has to be used to import food.

There will continue to be a large and, it is hoped, an expanding international trade in agricultural products. Temperate-zone countries cannot produce some tropical products, and vice versa. Some densely populated countries will never be self-sufficient in food production. The first objective for exporting countries should be to meet domestic food needs. Second, they should encourage diversification of products and responsiveness in the allocation of resources to export production so that shifts between crops to take advantage of changes in world demand and prices will be possible. To achieve this flexibility, they need a developed agriculture and facilities for the collection and dissemination of economic information.

Increased Demand for Industrial Products. The slow growth in the domestic market is one of the chief stumbling blocks to more rapid industrialization in many developing countries, which, typically, have only two classes—the very rich and the very poor. The absence of a large middle class limits the market for consumer goods. Some developing countries have tried protective tariffs or complete exclusion of imports to encourage domestic industry, but, with a small proportion of the population as consumers, even a completely protected industry soon runs out of customers.

Increases in the output and efficiency of agriculture result in higher farm incomes and enable farmers to buy more production items and consumer goods. This process of shifting from self-sufficiency within groups to economic interplay among groups has been an important feature of agriculture's contribution to economic growth in the United States. It is an extremely important element in the progress of the developing countries.

Many planners have stressed only the development of markets for farm products. I think this is a mistake. Without motivation, farmers will not do a more efficient job of producing. The means of self-improvement must be available to them. Some of these means will be found within the traditional rural community. For instance, farmers may use added earnings to increase the size of their holdings where land is available, improve their houses, or own better-quality animals. Other acquisitions (desirable for their usefulness and status value) must come from outside the rural community. Among these are industrial consumer goods, which might include such simple things at first as bicycles, cloth, and radios, and later refrigerators and other items.

I have seen many examples of incentives provided by the availability of goods for consumers. On my trip to Viet-Nam in early 1966, I visited with a farmer in Phan Rang who had received reclaimed land under the Vietnamese Government's agrarian reform program. He was growing a modified strain of Texas onions and earning roughly $800 per acre, compared with earnings of about $8–$12 per acre for rice in the same area. The market for onions at such prices is limited, of course, but the farmer was taking advantage of it while it was available. Among this farm family's most prized possessions were two new motorbikes—one red and the other blue. I could tell by our conversation that the opportunity to own these bikes repaid the effort required to increase his production and income. (Not unexpectedly, this farmer and others like him in Phan Rang would have nothing to do with the Vietcong. Theirs was a "safe" area, its people willing to fight to protect their newly acquired possessions.)

Many developing countries have discouraged the production and distribution of consumer goods, in order to save scarce resources for investment. Carried too far, this policy can be a mistake. Some consumer goods are necessary as a stimulus for people to save and to increase production and income.

A large part of the labor and capital employed in non-agricultural sectors of the developing countries is used for transporting, storing, and processing agricultural raw materials. Likewise, much industrial and commercial activity is concerned with agricultural supply industries—such as those furnishing tools, machines, fertilizers, pesticides—and with industries supplying consumer goods for rural people. When we count all the economic activities dependent upon agriculture, we find that it is the dominant force. If it remains stagnant, even rapid development in the industrial sector will not improve over-all economic conditions significantly.

STEPS OF THE DEVELOPMENT LADDER

Obviously, various countries are on different steps of the development ladder. Estimates of per capita income, even though not completely accurate, provide the best single indicator of national economic development. Agriculture's share of total employment provides an approximate indication of the level of agricultural development. Usually when more than one-half of the people of a country are engaged in farming, agriculture is still at a subsistence level. If we plot these two factors—income per person and the percentage of the labor force in agriculture—on the two axes of a chart, we find that the countries of the world cluster close to an imaginary line running diagonally across the chart. The most developed countries are at the upper right and the least developed at the lower left (see Chart 4).

What does the record show with respect to progress in agricultural productivity? Is agriculture moving forward in the

Chart 4

INCOME PER PERSON AND PER CENT OF
LABOR FORCE IN AGRICULTURE, 1962-64

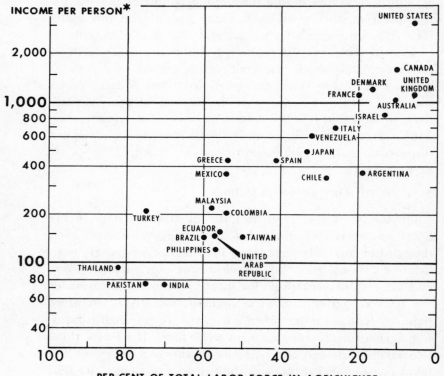

PER CENT OF TOTAL LABOR FORCE IN AGRICULTURE

*1962-64 U. S. DOLLARS.

U. S. DEPARTMENT OF AGRICULTURE

developing nations at a rate that will sustain satisfactory economic growth or has it been stagnating?

All countries achieved large increases in their total agricultural production between 1938 and 1963. This is true for developing as well as developed countries. But, as we have been stressing, population has also been increasing rapidly, especially in the developing countries. Although some of these countries have increased food production as rapidly as population in the last fifteen years, merely keeping food production abreast of population growth is not enough—it is not nearly enough. Most people in these countries are not eating sufficient food now, and very few are eating the foods that are essential for good nutrition.

Economic development sharply increases the total demand for food. It also brings about major changes in the types of foods demanded. As people move from country to city and earn larger incomes, they are not content to sleep off hunger. Nor are they able to forage from the land during periods of desperate food shortage or content to limit themselves to cereals and other starchy foods.

In the last decade, food production has not increased rapidly enough to keep pace with expanding economic demand for food in most developing countries. Total economic demand for food has increased 4–6 per cent a year for most countries, but annual increases in total food production have been much less. A few countries, including Greece, Yugoslavia, and Taiwan, have increased total agricultural production by 4 per cent or more annually during the last decade. All of these countries have placed high priority on developing agriculture, and the roads, schools, and power supplies that are so necessary. They are climbing the development ladder. What has been done in these countries can be repeated, with appropriate modifications, in other countries.

Although much remains to be learned about the interrelationships between agriculture and economic growth, we have

learned that nations cannot grow—nations cannot even survive—if agriculture is neglected.

COMPLEXITIES INHERENT IN AGRICULTURE

Agricultural development is not only critically important,
but also far more difficult to achieve than industrial development. In contrast to mining or oil production, for example,
spectacular successes achieved in a short period are rare in
agriculture. There is something about the nature of agriculture that sets it apart from other segments of the economy—
even in the more developed countries. In America, farming
has been regarded as a way of life. One would seldom apply
this term to other business enterprises. The difficulties and
complications of agricultural development as compared to industry help to explain why agriculture has been neglected in
some of the developing countries and why some agricultural
development programs have failed to meet the expectations of
the planners and their governments.

The greater importance of land to agriculture than to industry is one of the most obvious differences between the two.
Except for a few types of agricultural products, such as mush-
rooms, agricultural production requires the use of far more
land than any of its industrial counterparts. Few manufacturing plants occupy more than 50–100 acres, while providing
employment and livelihood for hundreds or even thousands
of families. Under conditions prevailing in American agriculture, an approximately similar land area—depending on loca-
tion—probably would not be sufficient to provide an acceptable level of income for more than one farm family.

It is said that farm people and their communities are tied
to the land. Because land stays put, farming capital tends to
be immobile. On the other hand, industrial capital has a high
degree of mobility. Plants can be constructed in an almost
infinite number of locations, and the managerial and labor

supply required to operate these plants is also highly mobile. Today, capital and technicians from the United States and many other countries are constructing and operating industrial plants all over the world.

Another difference between agriculture and industry is that industry can be imported, but agriculture has to be developed locally. It is possible and feasible for a country to import the bulk of an industrial complex—machines, management, capital, and much of the needed labor. And industrial technology has almost universal applicability. The same steel plant can work equally well in the United States or in India. In spite of acute shortages of human and physical resources, industrial development can proceed rapidly in developing countries. Gradually, local labor and management can be trained, and local sources of capital for plants and equipment can be generated with an uninterrupted flow of expanding production.

Such an approach is much more limited in agriculture. Although it has been used for years with certain plantation crops—bananas, coffee, tea—in the main, it does not apply to other kinds of farming. Certain types of technical assistance for training farmers and certain important production items, such as fertilizer, can be imported, but, by and large, the vast number of farmers tied closely to the land means that agriculture must be developed at home, within each country.

Another striking difference between agriculture and industry is the degree to which decision-making is concentrated in industry. In any one industry, there are rarely more than a few hundred firms and a few thousand persons concerned with the important operating decisions. In contrast, there are millions of farmers who are managers and decision-makers. Without government assistance and coordination, they seldom act in concert. This contrast in numbers is even greater for the developing than for the developed countries. Generally, in the developing countries, a much larger proportion of the population is engaged in agriculture. For example, the

United States, with a population of about 200 million, has approximately 3 million farm units, whereas India, with a population of more than 500 million, has more than 60 million farms.

It is obvious that the job of influencing decision-making in agriculture is very much larger and more complex than in industry. Not only are there many more units to work with, but they are dispersed over a much wider geographic area. This fact has an important bearing on the planning of agricultural research, education, and extension programs, and on arrangements for supplying such needs as credit, fertilizer, and seeds. Dispersal of farmers also complicates the marketing of agricultural products, which must be assembled from many relatively small producers, graded and processed, and then distributed to millions of consumers. Both in distance and functions, the agricultural producer is far removed from those who produce the items he needs for food production and from the consumers of the things he produces. Thus, compared with industry, the organization of agriculture as a business is much more complex.

Another feature peculiar to agricultural production is the importance of biological and natural phenomena. Farming is highly subjected to the vagaries of weather, insects, diseases, and a host of other factors that influence production and are difficult to control or predict systematically. One of the great contributions that science has made to agricultural production has been to provide measures for counteracting the adverse effects of these natural and biological phenomena. Thus, irrigation can prevent drought and contribute to more uniform production, while pesticides and certain cultural practices provide a reasonable degree of protection against insects, diseases, and other pests. The natural and biological factors that affect agricultural production are not static however. As old diseases are conquered, new ones arise. Technological advance is always necessary in agriculture to maintain a given level of efficiency and stability in production.

Altogether, agriculture is usually a much riskier business than industry. This higher risk helps to explain why farmers have a reputation for conservatism—particularly with respect to changing production practices. There is more resistance to changes that are costly to make than to those that are relatively inexpensive. Moreover, the farmer may change and then find that he has new problems. For example, he may decide to use fertilizer for the first time in a year of bad weather and poor crops. His return on the harvest may not be large enough to cover normal production costs, much less the added cost of the fertilizer. Thus, instead of increasing his income through the use of fertilizer, this farmer has increased his debt and the experience may make him reluctant to use fertilizer again. It is only as the long-run benefits of fertilizer become recognized on a widespread basis that resistance to its regular use breaks down.

Adoption of new practices in agriculture produces other complications. Often, many new materials and methods must be combined at once. Research has shown that better results are obtained when improved practices are used in combination, rather than separately. Thus, merely substituting a new variety of seed for an old one may not increase yields significantly. But improved seed combined with adequate amounts of water, fertilizer, and pesticides will outproduce older varieties even if the older ones also have the benefit of new production practices. This discovery has led to the so-called package programs for increasing agricultural production in India and Pakistan.

When all of the difficulties in improving agriculture are viewed together, it becomes evident that they are more numerous and more complex than those usually encountered in industrial development. But their being complex does not imply, as some pessimists have concluded, that nothing can be done. Much has already been done to improve agriculture in the developing countries of the world. Institutions for research, education, communications, and organization have evolved, and their work is beginning to show results.

For what can be attained from scientific research and the application of knowledge, the experience of the United States may be cited once more. From the time the Department of Agriculture was established, in 1862, until the late 1940's, although total food production increased greatly, there was little change in yields per acre or yields per man-hour of labor on farms. During these years, however, the U.S. Department of Agriculture and the state agricultural experiment stations were accumulating a vast amount of scientific information. We had also evolved a new concept in education—adult education through the Agricultural Extension Service. We had developed an efficient system for gathering and disseminating information. These provided the foundations for the take-off in agricultural production witnessed in the United States in the last twenty years. Since 1940, per capita output in agriculture has increased 275 per cent, compared with a 90 per cent increase for an American industrial worker.

What has happened to us is beginning to happen elsewhere. Some of the countries that began receiving technical assistance in agriculture twenty years or more ago are now progressing under their own initiative. Mexico and Turkey are examples of countries where agricultural technology has advanced and yields per acre and total production have risen sharply. Most technical assistance, however, whether from the United States, from other developed countries, or from international organizations, has been spread very thinly. Much more needs to be done.

We cannot turn our backs on agricultural development simply because there are many obstacles in the way and the rewards come slowly. The stakes are too high. Rather, we must face the problems for what they are—complex, frequently frustrating, and requiring tremendous human effort. With the new Food for Freedom program and strong emphasis on agricultural development in the AID program we are beginning to make more rapid progress.

There are few miracles in agricultural development—just lots of hard work. Neither the geographic nor the technological frontiers of the United States were crossed easily or without sacrifice. So it will be for the developing countries of the world—and for their partners. We must keep in mind, moreover, that these countries are being asked to do in a few short years what it took the United States and other developed countries a century to accomplish. The need for fast work, as both the developed and the developing countries face up to the task before them, increases the inherent difficulties of that task. To measure up to it will take all our resolve, patience, and intelligence.

❦

CHAPTER 4

The Why, What, and How
of Technical Assistance

❦

Earlier chapters have made it clear that the world faces a food crisis because man has not made good use of the resources available to him. The world has millions of people who are unemployed or underemployed. It has unused land that could be brought under cultivation, and millions of acres that could be made to produce much more abundantly. With the technology now available—but disregarding costs, political limitations, patterns of land ownership, and other limiting factors—production on land currently under cultivation could be stepped up two or three times. This increase would be enough to provide an adequate diet for the world's current population, with a reserve left over.

This chapter will show, by examples of what has been done, that the developing nations can improve their agriculture if they are determined to do so, and if we and the other rich nations will provide technical assistance. Later chapters will discuss the need for credit and capital, the tremendous contribution that private investors are making, and the place of voluntary and international agencies in technical assistance.

Let me repeat: Men, land, and knowledge can be brought together to banish hunger and malnutrition throughout the world. Only when we do this can we reach our goal of bettering the lives of people everywhere.

THE NEED FOR "KNOW-HOW"

Many in the developing countries are caught in a vicious circle of malnutrition, underemployment, and ignorance. The circle can be broken, but only by a world-wide effort. Technical assistance is an important part of that effort. While food from the developed world buys time, a vital, forceful program of technical assistance, with adequate capital support, can bring about an increase of food production throughout the world by exporting technical agricultural "know-how." But the task is not simple. It calls for decision, dedication, determination, and heavy investment.

Progress comes slowly and hard. It depends upon such diverse and sometimes unpredictable things as soils, climate, literacy levels, capital, cultural patterns, social and economic values, and world markets for agricultural commodities. But each of these is, or can be rendered, susceptible to change and adaptation. Over the long run, the changes and adaptations made will determine whether or not economic growth will take place. Each country must begin to improve its agriculture by drawing upon the knowledge and resources that it already possesses and by fitting new techniques into current practices. Since each country is unique, sound, individual policies and programs must be developed and adapted.

In most developing countries, a great gap exists between the intellectual elite and the actual farmers. Although most countries have excellent national universities, where highly trained specialists carry on laboratory research and produce learned papers, the number of agricultural experiment stations is woefully inadequate. We have about as many in the United States as there are in the entire developing world. This is one area in which we can assist.

EMPHASIS ON INCREASED PRODUCTION

Technical assistance in agriculture embraces the whole range of actions that can be taken to help the developing nations increase their total food production.

The emphasis now should be upon the production of as much food as possible from every acre as quickly and as efficiently as possible.

In most of the already densely populated developing nations new farmland is becoming scarce, but labor is plentiful. A plentiful supply of labor dictates intensive agriculture. Even where there is considerable industrialization, new factories do not employ masses of unskilled or semiskilled labor, as industry once did. Many jobs formerly filled by unskilled workers have been automated. Intensive agriculture, however, can still use many workers, and should do so in the regions where large numbers of unemployed and underemployed workers are available and where food crops are small in relation to needs.

For nearly 200 years, the rapid progress of industrialization in Western Europe provided a continuously expanding market for the raw materials of less developed countries, usually the commercial cash crops of plantations or the products of mines. But this market, with its opportunities for the developing nations to earn foreign exchange, began to decline about the time of World War II. Some commercial agricultural products, such as rubber, were, in part, replaced by synthetic substitutes. Others commonly described as commercial—for example, sugar, coffee, and cotton—are today often priced at or below the cost of production. It makes little sense to export these commodities at a loss and then have to import food. The aim of our technical assistance, therefore, in countries still concentrating on cash crops is simple: to change to farming for food.

Professor Setiadji Sastroamidjojo, a faculty member of Gadja Mada University, in Djakarta, Indonesia, a man with degrees in physics and nuclear engineering from the Massachusetts Institute of Technology and the University of California, has abandoned the laboratory for the plowed field and the milking shed. Not long ago he explained his reasons for doing so to a visitor. Indonesia, at this moment in its history, he feels, has more need for increased food production than for nuclear physics. His project, on a few acres of fertile land on the university campus, includes raising thirty-two head of Frisian dairy cattle, crossbreeding pigs, and growing corn. With no training in agriculture, Professor Sastroamidjojo began by reading manuals on dairy farming and hog raising. Today, he is not only introducing improved varieties of corn and producing livestock adapted to Indonesian conditions, but is also demonstrating that farming can be a money-making business.

The developed and the developing nations have lost time in a debate over whether to put limited resources into measures that will have an immediate effect or to put them into more basic measures that will help modernize farming over a longer period of time, with perhaps a more lasting effect upon increased food production. Both are needed, of course; but in most developing countries the immediacy of the crisis dictates a priority for actions that will increase food production promptly. For the United States, this priority means adjusting our technical-assistance programs to the specific needs of people and nations and emphasizing short-term research and its immediate application—as, for example, we did in El Salvador, on the west coast of Central America.

El Salvador has had a small amount of technical assistance in agriculture from the United States since 1942. First, an experiment station was established, with U.S. help. Since then, the Government of El Salvador has built institutions for agricultural research, education, and extension, and has had programs of land settlement, crop and livestock production, and credit to low-income farmers. These investments are now paying off. Despite rapid population growth, for the first time in its history El Salvador is producing all the corn it needs for human consumption. The yield of beans, the main source of protein in the Salvadoran diet, has been doubled through plant breeding. The U.S. Department of Agriculture technical-assistance team now working in El Salvador includes a land economist, an agricultural credit specialist, a marketing and planning specialist, an entomologist, a geneticist, a veterinarian, and a livestock specialist. One recent achievement is the control of the leaf-cutting ant, a vicious destroyer of crops. For about six cents, a Salvadoran farmer can buy from his extension agent enough insecticide to destroy an ant colony.

To meet food needs in the developing countries, the yields of food crops per acre must be increased dramatically. (Over the last twenty-five years, per-acre yields in North America have increased 50 per cent, in contrast with only about 7 per cent in Asia, and 8 per cent for all developing countries.) Each farmer must apply on his own land a package of practices specifically tailored to his soil, the local climate, and the insects and diseases that he must combat. But, before the individual can do this, such practices must be checked on test plots, using different combinations of plant nutrients, seed, water, and pesticides under controlled conditions. Then, when the best combination has been found, farmers must be shown how to use the new information. Both the testing and subsequent teaching require skill.

When technical and educational assistance are successful,

the results can be spectacular. In one region of Pakistan, an American scientist (recently returned from fourteen years' service overseas) found that the yields of both rice and sugar cane were sharply reduced by insects and plant diseases. He immediately began tests to determine which sprays would be most effective against these threats, and, in time, persuaded local government officials to help farmers spray their crops. Five years later, he found that all of the farmers were spraying, that yields had increased sharply, and that a local industry had grown up to supply and repair sprayers and furnish the necessary chemicals. Not least, the success of this program had made the farmers much more receptive to other changes.

All the good ideas and all of the applied research in the world, whether intended to increase crop yields or to improve animal husbandry, mean little unless they are adopted by the farmers. Sometimes, more than one effort is necessary. In the 1920's, an American missionary introduced improved chickens into a region in India. Many farmers began raising the new breeds, only to see their flocks wiped out by Newcastle disease. Later, a vaccine was developed to control the disease, and the farmers tried again, this time with chickens inoculated with the vaccine. Many farmers in the area became self-supporting poultrymen.

It is interesting to note that, since those early days, Peace Corps volunteers in other parts of India have helped build up a sizable poultry industry, numbering close to a quarter of a million laying hens. Thanks to these workers, many Indian farmers have seen how simple practices—such as keeping chickens penned, improved feeding, and sanitation measures—can transform scrawny, unproductive hens into good layers. In some cases, the degree of expertise need not be great if there is sufficient dedication to the task and if competent technical advice is available when special problems arise. A prominent newspaper reporter proudly described to me, at a banquet one night in Washington, D.C., how his Peace

Corps son, with a college degree in history, was teaching Indian farmers, with great success, to raise poultry.

MARKETING REFORMS

In some parts of the world, the greatest need is for immediate marketing reforms that will help farmers dispose of their products at a profit. Such improvements also aid urban people in getting more and better food, often at lower prices. In many countries, farm prices for staple commodities fluctuate as much as 70 per cent from the off-season high to a low immediately after harvest. Adequate transportation and storage facilities, and protection from insect and rodent damage during storage, would greatly reduce this price spread, with benefit to farmers and consumers.

Perishable products must either reach markets quickly or be processed to prevent spoilage. Dates, one of the oldest of the world's cultivated crops, provide an example. Unless protected in screened sorting sheds, they are attacked by a fly immediately after harvesting. They must also be fumigated during sorting and drying to keep them from becoming wormy and unfit for human food. Technical experts from the United States are now helping date farmers with these and other marketing problems.

In the early years of development planning, marketing of food crops was neglected by economists and policy-makers. As a result, even though production for domestic needs would have meant a better use of resources, and though there was a potential demand, farmers continued to produce commercial export crops. Today, enclaves of agricultural development are found in places where new processing facilities have been installed—either by private enterprise or by public or international agencies—to process foods for domestic consumption and to move them to market. To be successful, new processing facilities must be based upon careful analyses of market potentialities. The United States has developed this type of analysis to a high degree, and we should make it available everywhere as part of our technical-assistance program.

Among the examples of successful processing and marketing in the underdeveloped countries, the milk-processing plant in Calcutta, India, is outstanding. It is hard for Americans to imagine a city of more than 5 million people dependent for its milk supply on cows driven from door to door and milked, on order, for customers. But that was Calcutta in the mid-1950's. Under the sponsorship of the FAO, a team of dairy experts from the United States and other milk-exporting countries visited Calcutta in November, 1955, to help with modernization. The Government of India already had a long-term milk-development scheme for the city, but lacked the foreign exchange and technicians to carry it out. The plan was to remove the cows and milk buffalo to dairy farms and to build a modern dairy plant to process and distribute milk. The dairy experts saw in this plan an opportunity to increase milk supplies, quality, and consumption through the blending of locally produced milk and imported dry skim milk into a product called "toned" milk. Buffalo milk was particularly good for this purpose because of its very high fat content. The milk-exporting countries provided the dairy plant machinery, the technical assistance, and a reduced price for part of the dry skim milk needed for a period of three years. From that rather simple beginning, the Calcutta milk-processing scheme has grown into a complex of dairies and factories. Similar programs have been started in other Indian cities and elsewhere in Southeast Asia.

The most modern processing plants and storage facilities will serve no purpose without a transportation system. In fact, some of our technical assistance and capital has been going to help plan and develop transportation facilities. It is all too possible, under present conditions, for food to be plentiful at one place, with no means of transporting it to another place in the same country—or even in the same district—where it is desperately needed. Thus, transportation is another of the many problems that must be considered if our technical assistance is to aid the agricultural development of nations asking for our help.

APPLIED GENETICS: ONE SUCCESS STORY

In some areas of technology, as in applied genetics, the goals of long-term change and immediate results coincide. For example, the use of improved varieties of wheat and corn and the long-range scientific skills needed for developing even better varieties are working together to transform agriculture in many places. During the last fifteen years, Mexico's national average wheat yield has grown from thirteen to nearly forty bushels an acre. These increases are due in part to new varieties created in Mexico. The new varieties were developed through crosses between several standard wheats and semi-dwarf varieties from Japan, the object being to find disease-resistant varieties with short, strong stems, so that the wheat could be fertilized heavily and irrigated without the usual problem of lodging (falling over).

This development work was initiated by the Rockefeller Foundation, but is now entirely in the hands of Mexican scientists. The Foundation is collaborating in an international wheat-breeding program, headquartered in Mexico, aimed at sharing these advances with other nations. Some of the Mexican varieties of wheat—including Lerma Rojo 64A, Sonora 64, and others—are now being raised with marked success in Turkey, Afghanistan, India, and Pakistan. Yields have more than doubled, with many fields producing up to four times as much as under the traditional varieties. This new wheat seed is spreading around the world more quickly than any new variety in our history.

But, as the Rockefeller Foundation has pointed out, success with the new wheats requires more than new seeds. To get results with them heavy use of fertilizer, improved seed-bed preparation, proper depth of seeding, proper timing and adequate applications of irrigation water, and control of pests are necessary. And to persuade a farmer to do all these things requires educational follow-up.

IMPORTANCE OF FERTILIZER

A recent study shows that countries getting high yields of cereals use relatively large applications of fertilizer. For example, cereal yields per hectare in Japan and Taiwan, where large quantities of chemical fertilizer are applied, are three to four times as high as those in Pakistan and India, where relatively little fertilizer has been used.

The great majority of developing countries have an acute shortage of fertilizer. I have had a lot to say around the country and in this book about the food gap in the developing world. It is instructive to translate the food gap into a fertilizer gap. A 20 million–ton food gap is a 2 million–ton fertilizer gap! It's as simple as that. One pound of plant nutrients, used in association with water, pesticides, and suitable seed, can yield ten pounds of additional food grains. There is a one-year time lag between fertilizer and food. This year's fertilizer is next year's food. The cost of filling the food-fertilizer gap is reduced by two-thirds if it is filled with fertilizer, rather than with direct food aid. Plainly, the availability of fertilizer becomes a top priority, to which nearly every advanced country can contribute in a major way.

Fertilizer can be used effectively on almost any size farm, from the smallest to the largest. Many farmers in the developing world have become convinced that the use of fertilizer will give them a larger real income. Meeting the resulting demand has become one of the big problems in the war against hunger. Only a few years ago, fertilizer was a drag on the market in many of the developing countries, but it is now in strong demand in most areas. Recently, Indian villagers, queued up at a local fertilizer warehouse, are reported to have rioted when the supply of fertilizer was exhausted before their needs were met. Such unruly action is an encouraging development—a sign of progress.

Importation of chemical fertilizer is a drain on the limited foreign-exchange funds of the developing nations. The increased agricultural production resulting from the use of fertilizer is often consumed within the nation, rather than exported to earn more foreign exchange. In light of the food shortages, that is as it should be. But these countries still have the problem of paying for fertilizer. For some time, U.S. and World Bank specialists have been urging the necessity of establishing fertilizer plants in many of the developing nations. Some headway is being made, but availability of raw materials and problems of management and capital, as well as government attitudes, have hindered progress. These problems are discussed in greater detail in the next two chapters.

IRRIGATION AND RECLAMATION

Essential as it is, fertilizer is effective only where there is adequate water. Man's use of water resources must be made much more effective. Over two-thirds of the world's fresh water flows uselessly into the oceans. Irrigation agriculture, which originated in ancient Egypt and has been practiced in many parts of the world, helps. But irrigation has always been an inefficient user of water. Through many years of research, we have made considerable progress in using water more efficiently in the United States, particularly in the arid West. We have learned how to reduce waste of water by such methods as lining irrigation ditches, reducing evaporation by covering water storage areas with film, and controlling runoff through contour farming and the use of terraces. Also, U.S. experience in controlling salinity is being applied to irrigated areas in Africa, India, Pakistan, the Mekong River Basin, and other parts of the world.

One of the big problems occurring in irrigated areas is salinity. Irrigation water contains small quantities of salts. Unless the salts are flushed downward to ground water by rainfall or abnormally heavy irrigation, they are left in the root zone of the soil as moisture evaporates or is used by plants. After some soils have been irrigated for several years, they become saline, and yields decline.

When I visited Pakistan in 1966, I had the opportunity to see an interesting project where salinity was being controlled. Irrigation in West Pakistan had been practiced for seventy years under British rule. By 1960, more land was being abandoned annually because of excessive accumulation of salts in the soil and waterlogging than was being brought into production by the opening of new irrigated areas. President Ayub Khan of Pakistan had asked President Kennedy for help. In response, a team headed by Roger Revelle, at that time science adviser to the Secretary of the Interior, visited Pakistan and prepared a plan for rehabilitating 3 million acres of waterlogged land and 24 million acres of threatened arable land over a period of twenty to twenty-five years. It was decided to concentrate first on the development of areas where the potential returns would be highest.

The first Salinity Control and Reclamation Project (SCARP-I) comprised 1.2 million acres in the Punjab. About one-third of the land was affected by soil salinity. The first objective of the project was to stop, and then reverse, the salinization and waterlogging of the soil. Tube wells were sunk to lower the water table and provide additional irrigation water to leach excess salts from the soil by alternately flooding and draining the fields.

The United States furnished a large volume of technical assistance in getting this first project under way. It also supplied capital in dollars for the purchase of equipment for the tube wells, as well as Pakistani currency for other materials and labor. The project was planned in 1963, and work was begun in 1964. By the time of my visit, in July, 1966, exciting results were already evident. Waterlogging had been eliminated. Three-fourths of the 425,000 acres affected by soil salinity had been reclaimed and were again under cultivation. Yields per acre on all crops had increased by from 30 per cent to 150 per cent. The yield on 350 acres sown with Mexican wheat was nearly four times that of the best local varieties and compared favorably with wheat yields in Western Europe, which are the world's highest. Pakistani authorities expect the entire wheat acreage in the project to be planted with the Mexican variety in 1967.

The success of SCARP-I is certainly encouraging. It must be recognized, however, that this area, comprising only 4 per cent of the cultivated land in West Pakistan, received a heavy concentration of capital and technical aid and was chosen because of its known potential. Whether such improvement can be sustained in this region, or duplicated in less promising regions, is yet to be demonstrated. By 1967, SCARP-II, SCARP-III, and SCARP-IV had been planned, and pilot work was under way on SCARP-II and SCARP-III. On all of them, as on SCARP-I, to consolidate the gains more attention will have to be given to agricultural extension education, agricultural credit, marketing, and storage.

Much remains to be learned about the long-term effects of irrigation on soils. Unless massive investments are made in drainage to match investments already made in increasing water supplies, the loss of soils through salinization could permanently destroy agriculture on the Indus plain. Here again, competent research and effective advice and technical assistance will be of critical importance.

Whatever the cause of "lost" land, its reclamation is a slow and expensive process. Not only salinity, but also other forms of soil destruction, such as wind and water erosion, are difficult to combat. In some parts of the world, eroded land and ruined cities are all that is left to mark ancient civilizations. North Africa, once the breadbasket of ancient Greece and Rome, but for a long time mostly unproductive, can be partly restored through reforestation and water conservation. The Medjerda River Basin development in Tunisia is an example of what can be done. In ancient times, the hillsides of this area were forested and the lower valley was almost a swamp. But as men moved in to plant cereals and to graze their animals, the forests were felled. Erosion began to take its toll. Over the centuries, the topsoil carried to the sea by the river added nearly six miles of lowland to the Mediterranean coast. After World War II, Marshall Plan funds and aid by American technicians made it possible to begin controlling the river's floods and to undertake a program of intensive agricultural development. By 1957, the first dam had been completed, followed shortly thereafter by two others.

Today, the valley farmers produce vegetables, citrus fruit, wheat and other grains, and livestock. They need still more capital and technical assistance however. At present, this capital is being supplied by Kuwait, West Germany, and the United States. Technical assistance is coming from UNESCO, West Germany, and the United States.

PRICE POLICY

One of the difficult problems in developing countries, and one on which much work needs to be done, is price policy. I can say from hard-earned experience that prices can be controversial, even when decisions are backed by painstaking research and experience. Nevertheless, price policies that will encourage the adoption of more efficient practices in the short run, and the modernization of farming in the long run, are essential for every developing nation. Our technical-assistance programs should include agricultural economists to carry out the research necessary to formulate meaningful alternative economic policies. Obviously, farmers will not adopt new measures that cost more than they get in return from increased production; however, countries with large urban populations that demand cheap food face practical and urgent political difficulties in trying to establish sound price policies for agriculture. In some cases, the answer may be to subsidize such things as fertilizers, improved seed, and insecticides. In other cases, subsidies may be used to hold down consumers' food prices. One way or another, the producer must get an incentive price before he will apply new practices quickly. It is ironic that, until recently, this great capitalistic land of ours largely ignored this simple economic fact of life in our technical-assistance programs.

What Can Be Accomplished: Israel and Taiwan

Even as we emphasize immediate programs to increase food production, we must keep in mind long-term modernization of farming. Education is a slow but sure way to improve and modernize agriculture. Our cooperative extension service—one of the most widely copied of American agricultural institutions—has helped modernize American agriculture. With appropriate adaptations, similar systems are being established in some of the developing countries. Some extension services are using radio—and a few are even using television—to get knowledge and instruction directly to farm families. In many places, demonstration plots have been the most effective teaching devices. Even though these efforts may require years to bear fruit, we should go forward with them. They can be adapted to the particular circumstances of each recipient country that pledges its full assistance.

Israel and Taiwan provide examples of what can be accomplished with capital, technical know-how, and determination. The odds against success with Israel's agriculture were tremendous. When Moses described the Holy Land, it was "a good land, a land of brooks of water, of fountains and depths that spring out of valleys and hills." But when W. C. Lowdermilk of the Soil Conservation Service of the U.S. Department of Agriculture made a survey of this same area, in 1938, he reported that he found the soils of red earth washed off the slopes to bedrock over more than half the upland area. . . .

In the denuded highlands of Judea are ruins of abandoned village sites. . . . Where soils are held in place by stone terrace walls, the soils are still cultivated after several thousand years. They are still producing, but not heavily, to be sure, because of poor soil management.

At that time, the country was governed by Great Britain, under a mandate from the League of Nations. The great movement for the redemption of the promised land by Jewish settlers had already begun. Lowdermilk says that everywhere he went he was asked to advise on measures to conserve soil and water.

Israel's population doubled between 1949 and 1959, and much is heard of the ingathering of an additional million in the next ten years. Population is increasing at the rate of 3.5 per cent annually. The government has been settling many of the immigrants on collective and cooperative farms. For reasons dictated by national security, many new farm settlements are located in poor, hilly, and desert areas. The Government of Israel, however, assumes responsibility for providing farmers with the means of earning a living. In the first decade of statehood, government expenditures for agricultural development overshadowed those for any other sector of the economy. Special attention has been directed to agricultural education and extension programs to bring the results of agricultural research to the farmers. These programs have been successful, partly because the literacy rate in Israel is 90 per cent.

Israel's growth has been heavily dependent on receipts from abroad, including donations, foreign loans, reparation and personal restitution payments from West Germany, and aid from the United States. U.S. contributions have included substantial quantities of wheat, animal-feed grains, and seeds shipped under the Food for Peace program. These have served in several ways. Reliance on imported grain has relieved the Israelis of the necessity of devoting their limited agricultural land to grain production. It has made possible much larger livestock, dairy, and poultry industries than the land would otherwise support. A large portion of the Israeli pounds accruing from the sale of P.L. 480 grain imports has been funneled into agricultural, forestry, and nutrition research. In the first twelve years of Israel's statehood, its farm production increased nearly five times. Almost all of the land that can be cultivated with the available supply of water is being used.

Israel's present agricultural policy is to produce those commodities that can compete successfully in both domestic and world markets. A goal of doubled farm output for export in three to four years emphasizes fruits and fruit products, wines, vegetables, and bulbs and nursery stock. Increases in future U.S. commercial agricultural exports to Israel seem probable for such commodities as wheat, animal-feed grains, oilseeds, and tobacco. Israel is buying more and more of its agricultural imports with dollars.

Israel has benefited from our help. At the same time, the country has made determined efforts to help itself—efforts that have helped make Israel an independent nation in the world community.

Taiwan is another country that is showing results. I know of a soil conservationist from Kansas who went to Taiwan in the 1950's and served for eight years as adviser to the Chinese Government. With the assistance of a local blacksmith, he designed and built a soil scraper for constructing narrow terraces on the steep hillsides, using the draft power of one water buffalo. Then he drew up diagrams, specifications, and instructions for making and using the scraper. They were printed in Chinese and distributed throughout the hill country of the island. This and the efforts of many others have contributed to Taiwan's remarkable increase in agricultural productivity; Taiwan is now able to feed its people.

Taiwan was by no means an altogether underdeveloped country when the Nationalist Government took up residence there. For fifty years, beginning in 1895, the Japanese had pursued a policy of developing Taiwan's agriculture to provide food and raw materials for the Japanese Empire. World War II seriously disrupted the country's economy. The postwar repatriation of about 30,000 Japanese colonials removed most of the country's managerial and technical force; however, the immigration of more than 600,000 Chinese civilians—mostly technical, professional, and administrative personnel—from the mainland more than replaced the departed Japanese. The Japanese left mills, mines, hydroelectric power plants, transportation and communications facilities, and irrigation developments that gave Taiwan an initial advantage over many other developing countries.

Postwar reconstruction of Taiwan's economy began in earnest in 1949. Japanese-owned land and industries turned over to the Chinese Government at the end of the war provided the initial support for a program of land reform that transferred the ownership of farmland to the farmers and much of the ownership of industry to Chinese civilians. The U.S.–Chinese Joint Commission on Rural Reconstruction, established in 1948, administered a large part of the agricultural program. Unlike economic development and planning boards in many developing countries, the Joint Commission had real power through its control of funds channeled into agricultural development. It provided the opportunity for a continuous dialogue on policy formation between top-level U.S. advisers and their Chinese counterparts.

During the first part of the postwar period, agriculture received high priority in the allocation of development funds, and much of the nonagricultural development was of indirect benefit to agriculture. For example, industrial development stressed the construction of fertilizer plants; investments were made in improved transportation; and human resource development improved the health and raised the educational level of the rural, as well as the urban, population. In Taiwan today, there is not the division between a primitive, poverty-ridden agriculture and a progressive, prosperous industrial sector that hampers many developing countries. During 1953–64, Taiwan had an average annual increase of 5.5 per cent in agricultural production. Food production has kept up with population increases—no minor achievement, since Taiwan has had one of the highest rates of population growth in the world. The country is now working on population control.

The heavy investment of both U.S. and Chinese Government funds in agriculture and in human resources laid a sound foundation for rapid industrial growth, financed increasingly by private investment. Thus, for ten consecutive years, Taiwan has achieved a 6–10 per cent increase in gross national product. U.S. aid to Taiwan was shifted from grants to loans in 1961, and was officially ended on June 30, 1965.

AMERICAN AGRICULTURISTS ABROAD

The developing countries do not have the supporting institutions that most of us in the United States take for granted. Here, an agricultural technician is usually a specialist. When he faces a problem outside his own field, he consults another specialist—perhaps from a land-grant college or experiment station only minutes away by telephone. In a developing country, there are few telephones outside major cities. Mail to the nearest experiment station may take a week or longer. Technicians preparing to serve in developing countries must learn, or relearn, the basic scientific principles of agriculture and animal husbandry. They have to be generalists as well as specialists.

The technician in foreign service must know the country and the people that he is to serve. He must appreciate their strengths and understand their needs. Many developing countries have very sophisticated cultural heritages, but their value systems may be different from ours. Part of the job of the technician is to find out how his scientific know-how can be adapted to fit the cultural patterns of his host country. He must be oriented to count his achievements, not in projects inaugurated or completed, but in techniques acquired and put to use by his counterparts. The object of technical assistance is to plant and cultivate ideas and knowledge in the minds of others, and he is a success in his job to the degree that he is able to teach those who are or will be teachers.

Through more than twenty years of experience in technical assistance, we have drawn upon experts from the Department of Agriculture and the land-grant colleges. These men, many of whom were born and raised on farms in an era when farming was more an art than a science, are now rapidly reaching retirement age. They number in the hundreds. Their replacements must number in the thousands if we are to accomplish the task before us. We have emphasized the training of engineers for the space race. We must now emphasize the training of agricultural scientists for the world-wide race in which technical assistance is pitted against starvation.

CHAPTER 5

❦

Capital for
Agricultural Development

❦

The United States has a long history of providing economic aid—both technical and capital assistance—to other nations. Although we made loans to our allies in World War I, our first large-scale foreign economic-aid effort, as noted earlier, was in the post–World War II period, with the Marshall Plan. A comparison of the Marshall Plan period from 1949–52 with the AID program from 1961–64 illustrates the magnitude of our economic-aid effort, and its burden on our country. In the years 1949–52, the United States authorized a total of $15.2 billion for foreign aid, of which $13 billion went for economic aid and $2.2 billion for military aid. The approxi-. mate population in the aid-receiving countries was 313 million. By comparison, U.S. foreign-aid authorizations during the 1961–64 period amounted to $18.3 billion, of which $15.3 billion went for economic aid and $3 billion for military aid. The approximate population in the aid-receiving countries was 2.2 billion.

Two points are worth highlighting. First, from the late 1940's to the early 1960's the level of U.S. foreign aid changed little. There was no great change in the level of military assistance, and only a small increase in the level of economic assistance. Second, the number of people affected by U.S. foreign aid increased sevenfold—from about 313 million to 2.2 billion.

It is interesting to compare U.S. economic-aid efforts during the two periods from two points of view—the size of U.S. aid efforts relative to our own productive capacity and the volume of aid authorized per person in the recipient countries (see Table 1). The average annual economic-aid appropriation during the 1949–52 period was $3.2 billion, compared with $3.8 billion in the 1961–64 period. But when we adjust for price-level changes between the two periods, the average annual appropriation in the 1949–52 period was $4.6 billion in 1961–64 prices, or nearly 20 per cent higher than the 1961–64 average. The level of economic aid can be related to the total output of goods and services in the United States and expressed as a percentage of our gross national

TABLE 1

COMPARISON OF U.S. ECONOMIC-AID EFFORTS, 1949–52 AND 1961–64

Item	*1949–52*	*1961–64*
Total economic aid (*in millions of dollars*)	12,994.50	15,322.50
Average aid per year		
(*in millions of dollars*)	3,248.60	3,830.60
(*in millions of 1961–64 dollars*)	4,575.50	3,830.60
Average aid per capita in recipient countries		
(*in dollars*)	10.39	1.72
(*in 1961–64 dollars*)	14.63	1.72
Average U.S. GNP (*in billions of dollars*)	293.60	554.20
U.S. economic aid per year (*as a percentage of GNP*)	*1.11*	*0.69*
Average U.S. consumer price index (*1957–59 = 100*)	*86.40*	*122.10*
Approximate population in recipient countries		
(*in millions*)	312.70	2,217.00

product (GNP). This gives a rough measure of the economic-aid burden on our productive capacity. Economic aid
amounted to 1.11 per cent of the GNP in 1949–52, compared
with 0.69 per cent in 1961–64. The level of U.S. economic
aid in the receiving countries amounted to $14.63 per person
during the 1949–52 period (at 1961–64 prices); in the 1961–
64 period, this figure was $1.72. In recent years, this level has
further decreased; a sharp reduction took place in fiscal year
1968.

We should keep in mind that the major objective of economic aid under the Marshall Plan was to rebuild the productive capacity that had been destroyed during the war. The
countries receiving foreign economic assistance during that
period were, for the most part, developed nations prior to
World War II. They had the capacity to absorb effectively
large amounts of economic assistance. Their recovery record
was remarkable. Today, the nations that we helped to rebuild
are in a position to join with the United States in assisting the
development of the rest of the world.

THE CHANGING NATURE OF AID

Obviously, the developing nations of today are far behind
the Western European nations of the 1940's. Their problems
are quite different. Many of them do not have sufficient rates
of capital accumulation, either from internal savings or export earnings, to support the desired growth rates for the
economy, and particularly for agriculture. Thus, they must
turn to outside sources of capital and credit.

Countries at a relatively low stage of development do not
have the capacity to absorb effectively the amounts of assistance per person that we gave to the Marshall Plan countries.
It was said a few years ago, with some truth, that there were
more international credit resources available than there were
"bankable plans" in the developing countries to use the capi-

tal. But the picture is changing rapidly. Today, the reverse is true. For example, according to a recent report of the Inter-American Development Bank, agricultural output in Latin America should rise at the rate of 5 per cent a year. This pace requires that capital investments each year be about 100 per cent greater than those made in 1966. Bankable plans have already been made for at least part of this increase.

The decline in the U.S. foreign-aid effort does not necessarily reflect a unilateral movement away from the concept and principles of foreign economic assistance; but it is clear that there is substantial impatience with foreign assistance in the United States. Grass-roots disenchantment with aid programs is reflected in Congress, where each year it is more difficult to get appropriations for aid.

Our foreign economic-aid program is keyed to breaking the bottlenecks of economic development and achieving faster rates of growth in the countries receiving assistance. Progress has been much slower than we expected. Many countries have not done enough themselves to increase their capacity to absorb effectively more foreign economic assistance or to achieve the economic growth targets that they have set. For this reason, our new foreign-aid legislation stresses the self-help principle. We stand ready and willing to help those countries that have demonstrated a sufficient degree of willingness to help themselves. This means that the United States intends to do its share to provide the amount of technical and capital assistance that can be absorbed effectively in countries that break the bottlenecks to economic development.

Obviously, the United States has the capacity to supply much more assistance to the developing nations. We are a rich nation, but that does not absolve us from the responsibility to be prudent. The American people are generally patient and generous. Nevertheless, our taxes are high, and our needs at home are great. Riots in our larger cities in recent years have highlighted the need for enormous investments at home to provide education, training, and jobs for our own disadvantaged people.

The American voters are increasingly insistent that our foreign aid bring measurable results and assurances that we will not have to carry this burden forever. Developing countries must realize that they have to compete for our resources. They will lose out unless they demonstrate the will to do a better job and convince American voters that additional economic assistance will produce substantial gains in economic development.

In the past, few developing countries have put enough capital into agricultural development, and we have tended to go along—mistakenly, I believe—with plans and programs that have given agriculture a low priority because it lacks prestige. We must urge developing countries to put more capital into agriculture—and here we must stand ready to help. Outside capital assistance may take the form of direct investment in agricultural projects. Or it may be required to help create the agricultural credit institutions necessary to finance modern development.

In a discussion of the capital needs for rapid agricultural development, it is not always meaningful to distinguish between investments that take place specifically within agriculture and those that are required for total economic development. Many investments required for nonagricultural development—including those in heavy industry, consumer-goods industry, and, particularly, transportation and communication facilities—also directly benefit agriculture. Improvement of transportation systems means that farmers have better access to markets for their products and to the goods that they wish to buy. Dependable transport helps to maintain the quality of farm products, with greater returns to producers. A modern communications system provides prompt dissemination of market information to producers. Equally important, it helps to keep farmers informed of new and improved practices.

Heavy industry provides many essential products for agricultural development. These include steel for piping, power equipment, and building material; diesel and electric motors; tractors; and other farm machinery. Fertilizers and pesticides are other industrial products that are vital to agricultural development. The availability of reasonably priced consumer goods provides an incentive for cultivators to improve their economic position in order to gain the means with which to buy items desired by their families.

While it may be impossible to determine the full extent of capital investments affecting agriculture, we can draw some conclusions about the priority accorded to agriculture by the way in which AID funds have been allocated. In fiscal year 1964, food and agriculture received $119.5 million, out of a total of $1.1 billion for economic development, i.e., less than 10 per cent. Thus, only four years ago, economic aid to agriculture was small compared with other programs and woefully inadequate compared with needs. The willingness of the United States to accept the low status assigned to agriculture by most of the recipient countries was, in my judgment, tragic. We should have been trying forcefully to convince leaders in these countries that agricultural development comes first. We should have insisted that a larger share of our help had to go to improving food production.

Since President Johnson placed emphasis on self-help in 1964, there has been a change in U.S. policies and programs for agricultural development. Today, the agricultural needs of the developing countries are getting priority. As a matter of policy, we are emphasizing the importance of agriculture to every developing country with which we cooperate. In many cases, we are insisting that they revise their plans and put more resources into agriculture. AID officials, with the full cooperation of the Department of Agriculture, are giving careful attention to agriculture as they develop country plans for cooperating nations. In 1967, agriculture's share of AID economic-development funds was $504 million—four times as much as it was in 1964.

Several types of bilateral aid are provided by the United States: technical assistance, development loans, development grants, and supporting assistance. Almost all aid to agriculture falls into one of the first three categories. Of these, technical assistance has already been discussed.

DEVELOPMENT LOANS AND GRANTS

Development loans bear very low interest rates. Minimum terms set by Congress are 1 per cent interest for the first ten years and 2.5 per cent for the remaining thirty years of the loan. On June 11, 1967, AID reported that more than one-fifth of the total amount loaned since 1948 had been repaid. Loans may be made to finance fertilizer plants, dams for electric power and irrigation, and marketing facilities. Other loans finance such necessary imports as improved seed, fertilizer, or pumps for irrigation.

Development grants, which constituted a large part of Marshall Plan aid, have been declining since the European recovery period. They are gifts, usually designed to support technical-assistance programs by providing the materials needed by the technicians for demonstrations and pilot projects. Today, most development grants from U.S. funds are made through the Alliance for Progress.

In July, 1966, the Development Assistance Committee (DAC) of the Organization for Economic Cooperation and Development (OECD) met in Washington, D.C., for the first time. (Member nations of the OECD include most of those in Western Europe, and Japan, Canada, and the United States.)

It was also the first time that this committee had given special attention to agricultural development. The governments present pledged increasing attention to the problems of agriculture. The fact that this meeting was held is a hopeful indication that in the future other developed countries will make more substantial financial contributions to agricultural development.

Although food and agriculture dominated the agenda of the first DAC meeting on the North American continent, considerable attention was given to the terms on which aid is extended and the effect that these terms are having on the debt burdens of the recipient nations. There was considerable feeling that interest rates are too high and repayment periods too short. Some softening of terms has taken place recently, but the aid terms of most of the other Free World donors remain significantly harder than those of the United States. Their interest rates are generally higher and their maturities are shorter.

The debt repayment burden of the developing countries now totals around $5 billion annually and is rising by about 15 per cent each year. The DAC has established a working party to study this problem and to strive actively for better terms in both official and private credits. Unless more flexible foreign-assistance policies are adopted that gear the terms of loans more closely to the credit needs and debt-carrying capacity of each recipient nation, the effectiveness of aid efforts will be sharply reduced.

ADDITIONAL INVESTMENTS REQUIRED

Future needs for capital investments in the less developed countries are tremendous. The Panel on the World Food Supply of the President's Science Advisory Committee has estimated that to double agricultural output in the developing countries between 1965 and 1985—the target that they set as necessary—would require the following additional investments:

$17 billion for mining, manufacturing, and distribution of fertilizer,

$0.3 billion for production and processing of improved seed,

$1.9 billion for the production and distribution of pesticides,

$2 billion for the manufacture of farm machinery.

These figures add up to $21.2 billion in total additional investments. And they do not include the cost of obtaining improvements in water and soil management, education and training of agricultural personnel, research, and marketing, storage, and transportation facilities.

Clearly, the world's food and agriculture needs are too large for any one developed country to tackle alone. A concerted effort is necessary by all of the wealthier nations. Each nation can do more individually than it has done, and much more can be done through cooperative international efforts. A steady increase in the amount of capital and credit provided through such international agencies as the World Bank, the International Development Association (IDA), the Inter-American Development Bank (IDB) and the European Development Fund (EDF) is encouraging. The most recent additions to the growing family of regional banking institutions are the Asian Development Bank and the African Development Bank. The Asian Development Bank began operation on December 19, 1966, with a subscribed capital of $965 million and thirty-one member nations, nineteen of them Asian. The African Development Bank, with twenty-nine member nations, made its first loan on August 8, 1967, to Kenya, to help in completing road links with Tanzania and Uganda.

The multilateral share of the total Free World aid flow has

increased significantly over the past several years. It is the policy of the United States to cooperate in such multinational efforts. The U.S. share of official contributions to multilateral agencies now ranges from 32 per cent of World Bank subscriptions up to 43 per cent of the subscribed ordinary capital of the IDB. (We do not participate in the European Development Fund and other European multilateral assistance programs.)

The United States has been a leader in seeking improved international coordination of bilateral aid. We were instrumental in formulating the Development Assistance Committee of the OECD, the central review body for major Free World aid donors. And we have participated from the outset in the aid consortia and consultative groups set up by the World Bank and by the OECD for India, Pakistan, Turkey, Greece, and, more recently, Colombia, Nigeria, Sudan, and Tunisia. During fiscal year 1966, 85 per cent of all AID development loans in Asia and Africa was committed through these multinational consortia or consultative groups. The United States is one of the charter members and a subscriber to the new Asian Development Bank, with headquarters in Manila.

All U.S. Government capital assistance to Latin America is provided within the international framework of the Alliance for Progress. The Inter-American Committee of the Alliance for Progress (CIAP) is rapidly becoming a very useful forum for the coordination of assistance to Latin American countries. The activity of the CIAP, and the World Bank's expressed willingness to expand its role as a sponsor of multinational consultation, will greatly strengthen the international framework within which a substantial portion of U.S. bilateral aid is already provided.

In summary, the United States has made a very large capital contribution to the economic development of other nations, particularly during and since the Marshall Plan period. Today, we are carrying a smaller foreign-aid burden than we did fifteen years ago. As a nation, we could do more. So could other developed nations. But in the interest of wise and efficient use of resources, before we invest more of what we have, many developing countries will have to demonstrate their willingness and ability to do a better job in the future than they have done so far. They must demonstrate to the world that investing in their economic development will produce the results necessary to make them self-sufficient.

Governments do not command all the capital resources and human skills that are required for the tremendous task of economic development that lies ahead. Private resources, too, play a key role, and, as the next chapter suggests, can be increasingly important. Developing and developed nations alike must realize this fact and intensify their efforts to mobilize those privately owned resources that can help meet capital requirements in agriculture and related industries.

❦

Private Investment

❦

The period between World War I and the end of World War II was a low point in international economic development. Many of the gains of the preceding century were lost as commercial agriculture, which had become well established in many regions of the world, progressively deteriorated and large areas reverted to jungle or to subsistence farming. European investments were expropriated in many developing areas, and European managers and technicians expelled.

Since the end of World War II, private capital has been reluctant to invest in developing countries. The risks have been too great, and nationalistic restrictions on the operation of foreign business have been too severe. Also, some of the developed countries have tax structures that restrict the accumulation of venture capital; if a company makes an investment that pays off handsomely, much of the profit may be taxed away. As a result, international investment has been more and more through the international banking institutions and through bilateral borrowing, discussed in the previous chapter.

In recent years, there has been a slight upward trend in the flow of private investment from developed to developing countries, but this flow has been erratic. This has been as true for private investment from the United States as for that from other developed countries (see Table 2). Most important, the flow of private investment capital to the developing countries has not kept pace with rapidly increasing needs.

TABLE 2

NET FLOW OF PRIVATE FINANCIAL RESOURCES FROM DEVELOPED
COUNTRIES[a] TO LESS DEVELOPED COUNTRIES, 1956–66

Year	Total	United States
	(in millions of U.S. dollars)	
1956	2,881	1,230
1957	3,692	2,009
1958	2,822	1,275
1959	2,698	954
1960	2,958	1,042
1961	3,061	1,099
1962	2,450	812
1963	2,382	880
1964	3,208	1,325
1965	4,075	1,873
1966	3,422	979

SOURCE: *Development Assistance Efforts and Policies,* 1966 and 1967 reviews.
[a] Fourteen OECD members—Austria, Belgium, Canada, Denmark, France, Germany, Italy, Japan, the Netherlands, Norway, Portugal, Sweden, the United Kingdom, and the United States—and Australia.

Developing countries not only lack capital, but the necessary technical and managerial skills to utilize investment efficiently and effectively. One of the major advantages of foreign private investment is that it brings to the developing nations a package of capital and skills that can be put to work promptly and that gets results quickly. The skill, know-how, and determination of successful private business can be much more widely used in the developing countries. Here is a large resource of inestimable value that so far has been barely touched.

Some Problems for Businessmen

At the first International Agribusiness Conference in Chicago, on May 10, 1967, I stated that a communications gap exists, which acts as a barrier to an increased flow of private investment to developing countries. American "agribusiness," as the industries related to farming are called, has never been reluctant to accept the challenge of promising new opportunities. Countries with food deficits are beginning to welcome private investment from abroad. What, then, is preventing a large-scale transfer of this important segment of American capital, management, and technology?

Doing business in a developing country is far different from doing business at home. It is not enough to turn out a satisfactory product, service, or process. The American businessman must understand local political, economic, and social conditions; only then can his firm communicate effectively with its customers, employees, partners, and the host government. Companies that understand these requirements have generally done well. The first goal for private business interested in investing abroad should be to establish good communications in the developing countries.

Despite the problems that exist, many examples of effective private investment can be given. One of the most noteworthy is the role of private enterprise in fertilizer production and distribution. The developing world lacks fertilizer, yet both leaders and farmers have only recently realized its critical importance in increasing crop yields. There is little or no fertilizer technology in the developing nations. Also lacking is access to sufficient foreign capital or foreign exchange to build the modern fertilizer plants that are needed. Industrialists in the developed nations are aware of the growing fertilizer needs of the developing nations, and they know that making fertilizer available to farmers and promoting its use is one of the keys to agricultural development.

The experience of an American oil company in the Philippines is pertinent. This company built a fertilizer plant that went into operation in February, 1966. Even before construction was begun, the company hired salesmen and agronomists, so that the distribution system could be ready by the time the plant was producing. Market studies were made to determine appropriate types and quantities of fertilizer. More than 70 per cent of the farmers were using no fertilizer and had little or no knowledge of it. To reach them, the company launched an educational campaign using radio programs, pamphlets, film strips, and demonstrations. More than 100 farm demonstrations were started in December, 1964—a year and two months before the first bag of fertilizer was produced by the new plant. Throughout the Philippines, company-owned warehouses and independent retail outlets were established to assure that supplies would be available at the right place and time. The retail outlets, known as agroservice centers, carry pesticides, certified seeds, and farm implements, as well as fertilizers. Dealers must provide adequate storage and transportation for delivery of purchases and must participate in concentrated training by the company's technical and sales personnel. The company provides seventeen agronomists and thirty-two agronomist-salesmen who travel continuously, visiting dealers and farmers. There were 400 agroservice centers in operation by the end of 1967, and more are planned—so that a farmer anywhere in the Philippines can have his order for fertilizer filled within twenty-four hours.

American companies are also building fertilizer plants in Korea, Pakistan, India, Malaysia, Iran, Jamaica, and other countries. But fertilizer production is big business; it requires an investment of many millions of dollars. The Philippine plant—a relatively small one—cost $31 million. Larger plants may require investments of $60 million or more. This kind of investment is not attractive to private capital where there is economic or political instability.

The experience of an American feed-processing company provides a good example of both the contribution that can be made by private industry and some of the problems to be met and overcome. When this company moved into Colombia, in 1958, its first move was to establish a mill to provide balanced animal-feed rations so that Colombian farmers could supply increasing urban demands for meat, milk, and eggs. The company started building a sales and distribution system at the same time, training local salesmen in animal nutrition and Colombian businessmen in commercial distribution techniques.

It soon became evident, however, that the feed mill was drawing corn away from direct human food consumption. Production and consumption of corn were so evenly balanced that the purchases by the feed mill threatened to create a scarcity of food. The company shifted to milo as a feed ingredient and by guaranteeing a cash market to nearby milo growers, as well as providing technical production guidance, selected seed, and financing, successfully established this crop.

Next, the need for improved strains of poultry became apparent, leading the company into helping with the establishment of another new local industry—a breeding and hatchery operation to produce hybrid chicks. Then, an organization for processing and marketing poultry was set up. The American company provided advice and education for everyone: the farmer, the hatcheryman, the poultry processor, and the distributor. The company and the people that it was dealing with benefited from the research of foundations and from the cooperative attitude of the Colombian Government in clearing away obstacles. From the start, the company trained

Colombians to fill positions in its expanding organization. Today, it employs nearly 600 Colombians and only two Americans.

Other examples of successful American private investment in developing countries include the production of high-protein foods in Brazil, Colombia, Mexico, and Hong Kong and the manufacture of farm machinery in Mexico, India, Argentina, and the Philippines.

In spite of the success stories, an unfavorable climate for foreign private investment still exists in many developing countries. Although regrettable, this is understandable. Attitudes in developing countries are frequently based upon unpleasant experiences with private enterprise under colonial rule or with economic imperialism. Frequently, revolution has been directed against outside economic power as well as against political power. Espousal of private enterprise by the United States is seen by many Asians, Africans, and Latin Americans as a Trojan horse intended to impose on them new political and economic bondage. Nevertheless, some developing countries have noted the unhappy consequences of state ownership and have contrasted them with the successes of modern, dynamic private enterprises. For example, in the execution of each of India's three five-year economic-development plans since 1951, the private sector has responded more dynamically, and the public sector less so, than the plan had projected. As a result, each successive plan has assigned a larger role to the private sector. The trend in a number of other countries, including Mexico and Pakistan, has been in a similar direction.

The experiences of the developing countries in agriculture particularly highlight the problems of disequilibrium between the public and private sectors. In many cases, the governments have attempted to revive a stagnant agriculture through a combination of irrigation and public investment in such facilities as roads. Incentives, in the form of consumer goods and higher prices for agricultural products, have been neglected. The manufacture and distribution of production needs—such as fertilizer, pesticides, and implements—has often been a monopoly of the government. Profits from the sale of these products have been expected to finance public activities—thus resulting in high prices. As might have been anticipated, high prices have held down their use.

The United States has been trying to bring about a change in the unfavorable attitudes and policies toward foreign private investment. The new Food for Peace Act (the 1966 revision of P.L. 480) specifies that one criterion for judging whether a country is trying to help itself is the "development of agricultural chemical, farm machinery and equipment, transportation, and other necessary industries through private enterprise."

This requirement has resulted in some criticism that the United States is trying to force its free-enterprise system on other countries. Actually, the motive in establishing this criteria was not to sell free enterprise as such, but to get things moving. In most of the developing countries, the efficiency of publicly owned industries serving agriculture has been so low that it has held back progress. What Congress really meant was "we want results." We must realize however, that we are dealing with sovereign nations and proud peoples. The most effective inducement to change is usually quiet diplomacy rather than ultimatums, legislative or otherwise. Nothing succeeds like success itself, and the most effective pressures lie in the stories of what private enterprise is accomplishing in other developing countries.

There are hopeful signs that the food-deficit nations are coming to recognize time as a critical factor. If they are to feed their people, they cannot wait for their own industries— state or private—to accumulate the needed capital and technical skills to build desperately needed agricultural supporting industries, such as fertilizer plants. If they are to make quick progress in agriculture, they have no choice but to turn to the vast reservoir of talent and capital available in the private industrial sector in foreign countries. This does not mean that they have to compromise their principles against foreign domination. Foreign investors are not usually looking for special privilege. Most of them are interested in finding profitable investment opportunities, without disproportionate risk, in a competitive atmosphere. Given the tremendous need for investment in developing nations and the knowledge that much will have to come from foreign private sources, it is only sensible that the developing nations make extra efforts, even when politically difficult, to accommodate outside investors. This can be done, and is beginning to be done, around the globe. Unfortunately, many foreign investors still remain skeptical.

In its economic-development assistance programs, the United States is trying in every way it can to allay suspicion on both sides in order to get investments moving. We have not found all the answers yet, but we are moving toward solutions. On the one hand, we should not ask the developing countries to permit monopolies or unfair practices. On the other hand, we cannot expect private capital to run undue risks from unstable governments and vacillating policies, attitudes, and philosophies concerning the proper place of the private sector in the economy. Somehow, we must find the "middle way." I think it can be done with the tools now available.

INDUCEMENTS FOR INVESTORS

Our government provides a remarkable group of inducements to potential U.S. business investors in developing countries. First on the list is the information center that AID maintains for businessmen. It keeps a catalogue of investment information on developing nations and identifies specific investment opportunities.

When a company becomes interested in one of these investment opportunities, AID will share the cost of making a feasibility survey. By January 1, 1968, 134 such surveys had been completed, and thirty-six had resulted in planned investments totaling $81 million. Some of the surveys that produced decisions not to invest are also proving valuable to AID, since they indicate where problems exist.

If the feasibility survey shows promise, AID is prepared to ease the burden on the company through its investment guarantee program. Investments in developing countries are often exposed to political and commercial risks in excess of those generally incurred in developed countries. Under the guarantee program, AID gives special protection to private U.S. capital. The oldest part of this program is the specific-risk investment guarantee, which offers protection against losses caused by inconvertibility of currency, expropriation, war, revolution, or insurrection. From its inception in 1948 through the end of June 30, 1966, food and agriculture projects protected by AID investment guarantees numbered 154, with a total amount of $774 million.

Before these guarantees are issued, the government of the host country must approve the investment. The specific-risk programs operate only in countries that agree that if the United States makes payment to an insured company, the U.S. Government is then entitled to act for that company in negotiations with the host country and to collect funds due to that company. Guarantees covering specific risks of inconvertibility of currencies and expropriation are available in seventy-eight developing countries. Of these, forty-four countries have signed agreements covering war risks. The use of the specific-risk guarantee program has been increasing rapidly.

In addition, AID offers extended-risk insurance that may

protect up to 75 per cent of a company's investment against any risk for which commercial insurance is not available. As of December 31, 1967, AID had insured eight projects, with a coverage of $67 million. This program has helped to attract long-term financing from American institutional lenders, such as pension funds and insurance companies. It is helping in the war against hunger by insuring fertilizer plants in Korea, India, and Brazil, and a fish packing plant in Somalia. A newly inaugurated program called "equity insurance" provides coverage of up to half of any losses incurred through bankruptcy or sale. This type of insurance should be attractive to smaller U.S. firms wishing to establish overseas branches.

AID also makes loans to private borrowers and intermediate credit institutions. An integral part of AID's private investment program is the Cooley loans, financed from local currencies generated from the sales of commodities under Title I of P.L. 480. Loans may be made to U.S. firms, subsidiaries, or affiliates for both agricultural and industrial development. During 1967, thirty-five loans in fifteen countries were authorized, totaling the equivalent of $29.5 million. Since the beginning of this program, 432 loans in twenty-five countries, totaling $370.5 million, have been approved. The credits authorized went to a wide variety of industries—such as baking, plastics, corrugated cardboard, and grain-storage facilities, in Israel; chemicals, steel, tires, and food processing, in Turkey; pharmaceuticals, poultry breeding, and food processing, in Pakistan; chemicals, glassware, building materials, motors, electrical equipment, tractors, and fish processing, in India; and food processing and dairy and poultry production, in Colombia.

Of course, the resources of all American personnel—ambassadors, economic counselors, agricultural attachés, the AID professional staff, and others serving in the developing countries—are always available to private enterprises interested in investing in development industries.

Congress has a heavy responsibility in mobilizing private enterprise for broader participation in economic development around the world. The Advisory Committee on Private Enterprise in Foreign Aid, chaired by Arthur K. Watson of International Business Machines and popularly known as the Watson Committee, made a number of recommendations that have been endorsed by the Executive Branch of our government and submitted to Congress for legislative action. The Eighty-ninth Congress passed legislation implementing several of these recommendations. It ratified the International Convention for the Settlement of Investment Disputes. It raised the statutory ceiling on investment guarantees against inconvertibility, expropriation, and military hazards from $2.5 billion to $7 billion, and relaxed certain other statutory limitations on investment guarantees.

Several recommendations that have not cleared the legislative process should be enacted into law. The Watson Committee has proposed an overseas-investment tax credit of 30 per cent of the amount of new investments in certain trades or businesses in eligible developing countries. Returns on investments in industrialized nations average substantially higher than returns on investments in most developing countries. Proposed legislation would correct this imbalance, and should increase U.S. investment in productive facilities in the developing nations.

In our tax laws there are many provisions for tax credits, depletion allowances, and depreciation that do not apply to overseas investments. In certain cases, tax-sparing laws of foreign governments are negated by U.S. tax laws. Also, our antitrust laws tend to inhibit cooperation and collaboration between corporations in making overseas investments. Congress should study both of these problems and remove bottlenecks by overhauling our laws and joining in international conventions or treaties.

Congress can also appropriate sufficient funds to AID to enable the agency to maintain and expand its services to American private enterprise in developing countries. The United States, through Congress, can lend its support to the principle of an international code for the fair treatment of foreign private investors. Such a code, to be acceptable to the developing countries, must include a reasonable statement of the obligations of the investors as well as of the obligations of the host countries.

The Watson Committee has recommended that AID expand its program of investment surveys and assist the developing countries in undertaking large-scale market and feasibility studies as part of a campaign to interest prospective local foreign private investors. It has also recommended that AID select a number of key aid-receiving countries for intensive study of ways to improve the investment climate and that an explicit program be developed to make investments in those countries more attractive.

The U.S. Government has been highly successful in formulating "model laws" in various fields. Such model laws have helped the efforts to develop uniformity in state laws, which has been important in promoting economic development within the United States. We have also participated actively in developing international covenants. Our laws in such fields as soil and water conservation, rural electrification, and cooperatives have been copied by some developing countries. The knowledge found in the United States and other advanced countries could well be employed in developing model laws for corporations, banking institutions, the inspection and grading of foods, and taxation. Such a body of model laws would be a valuable source book for the government of a developing country seeking to improve its investment climate.

INTERNATIONAL SUPPORT

International organizations, such as the World Bank, the working groups of the United Nations Conference on Trade and Development, and the OECD, have had much experience in dealing with problems of international investment. The International Convention for the Settlement of Investment Disputes, originally proposed by the OECD and developed by the World Bank, came into force late in 1966, with forty-six signatory nations. Such international organizations might seriously consider devoting more of their resources to research and programs designed specifically to promote and facilitate private investment. They should draw on the experience of all developed nations. U.S. programs of investment guarantees and insurance have demonstrated the feasibility of this kind of assistance. Such a program might well be launched by an international organization.

Private industry in the United States can help gear itself to international development by cooperative action to share its hard-won knowledge within its own ranks and with industry in other countries. The Business Council for International Understanding, founded in 1955, has carried on a worthwhile program of training middle- and upper-management personnel of U.S. corporations for assignments in the overseas operations of their companies. The Council has also cooperated with the State Department and foreign governments in arranging inspection tours of U.S. industrial installations at home and abroad by foreign management personnel.

The International Executive Service Corps is a nonprofit voluntary organization that recruits experienced American businessmen to fill positions in business operations in foreign countries. As an example of its activities, volunteers of long experience with a large U.S. food chain helped supermarket operators in Venezuela and Nicaragua to reduce costs through improved buying techniques and food cleanliness practices. AID encouraged the establishment of the International Executive Service Corps and continues to provide some financial assistance for it. Volunteers are paid by the businessmen of the host country at rates prevailing in their countries. This organization serves as a clearinghouse through which retired American businessmen can contribute their special skills and services to the war on hunger.

The scarcity of competent managerial personnel in developing countries and the political and psychological need to have their own people participate at a high level in the management decisions of companies operating on their territories make it imperative that managerial capacity be nurtured in the developing countries. Here, international business might well take a leading role, enlisting the support of foundations and universities in building up country pools of trained managers who would serve in both the public and private sectors. Some of our large American corporations have been noted for their in-service and company-sponsored training programs at home. An expansion of such programs into the foreign field is logical and possible. Even when an industry is working on contract for a foreign government or for AID, a training program to produce trained management capacity, perhaps even in excess of the immediate needs of the project, should be made a part of the contract.

There has been much talk of the possibility of consortia that will combine the resources of several private companies with different skills and know-how. Such combinations could move into a developing country to plan and carry out an overall action program to modernize agriculture. A typical consortium might include fertilizer and chemical producers, farm implement manufacturers, food processors and distributors, and even farm credit organizations. The group could pool talent, avoid duplication, and share risks. Perhaps an international body such as the World Bank could supply credit or insurance on risk capital for the participants.

Opportunities in Processing and in Protein

Recent activities in the nutrition and food-processing sector of the American agribusiness community are exciting and far-reaching. Food-processing and marketing technologies are one of the marvels of the twentieth century. Frozen foods, dehydrated foods, and even freeze-dried foods are commonplace in the United States. Dietetic foods, low-calorie foods, and foreign specialty foods are widely available. Every housewife is familiar with the end products in her supermarket, but few are aware of the technology and market organization that puts them there. This complex of grading, inspecting, transporting, processing, and distributing has been studied and copied by the other developed countries.

Except in a very few urban areas, food processing is almost exclusively a function of the individual homemaker in developing countries. The urban areas may be supplied largely by imports, but most food is consumed very close to the place where it was produced. Surpluses in one area and shortages in another, even within small countries, are not unusual. Instead of a national market where housewives may choose between items equivalent to California or Florida oranges, Maine or Idaho potatoes, and Washington or Virginia apples, one developing country may have hundreds or even thousands of local markets, not only for perishable foods, but for such staples as wheat and corn and, indeed, for all sorts of consumption goods. As Walt W. Rostow, special assistant to President Johnson, has pointed out, national markets are an essential ingredient of economic development. Although they cannot be organized over night, the need is clear in most of the developing countries.

Any discussion of food in the poorer countries inevitably

leads to protein. Research in nutrition has revealed a shocking "protein gap" in many developing nations. Many countries suffer from both insufficient total food supplies and from
a shortage of protein, particularly of good quality protein.
The average per capita daily supply of animal protein in food
deficit countries is nine grams, compared with forty-four
grams in countries with adequate supplies. Animal protein is
very expensive, because it is costly to convert grain to animal
products. It takes 1,600 pounds of grain per person every year
to provide the high-protein diet common in the United
States. This is four times the amount of grain available in the
developing world and means that, for the most part, the less
developed countries must use proteins from plants, rather
than animals. Fortunately, vegetable-protein production can
be expanded, using crops already grown in the countries
where protein is most needed for human food. Much of the
present supply of high-protein plant material in the developing countries is not now being used for human food because
of ignorance or lack of processing facilities. Soybean and peanut meals are excellent sources of protein; but they are now
used in many parts of the world only for animal feed or fertilizer—often in the very countries where there is a severe protein shortage for human food.

The American (and other) food-processing industries have
an opportunity and a challenge in this situation. Low-cost,
high-quality proteins can be produced from plant sources by
adding missing ingredients or by processing methods that
alter their chemical construction. Certain amino acids, which
are usually the missing ingredient in vegetable proteins, are
now being synthesized at costs that approach practicality.
When produced commercially, they can be added to cereal
foods to produce a nutritionally adequate diet. Already, the
food industry has been able to refine the proteins in oilseeds
into a product that can be manufactured into synthetic foods,
reproducing the texture, appearance, and taste of various ani-

mal-protein foods. Some of these tailored protein foods, such as synthetic bacon, are gaining consumer acceptance in the United States. Emulsions and beverages containing all the nutrients necessary for humans can be made to resemble any food customarily eaten or drunk anywhere in the world. Fortified with this kind of technical knowledge, the American food industry can market tailored food anywhere in the world where it is economically feasible.

It is important to distinguish between high-protein foods designed for use in relief distribution and those expected to win acceptance in the marketplace. In relief distribution, the recipients usually have no choice except acceptance or rejection. If the food is too different from the familiar, even a hungry man may reject it; otherwise, he will eat it. But in the marketplace, people make choices among many products. To win acceptance, a new product must be superior to its familiar counterpart in those qualities upon which consumers base their judgments. Rarely is nutritional value a deciding factor. Instead, measures like sweetness, viscosity, or chewability determine choices.

Food taboos and preferences exist in all societies and at all socio-economic levels. We have little understanding of food habits in many developing nations. Without such knowledge and understanding, it is very difficult to tailor foods to meet local requirements. Simple and obvious as this statement may appear, recognition of the fact has been obtained the hard way—through repeated misjudgments in various programs, at different times, in different parts of the world.

A new program shared by the Department of Agriculture and AID has enlisted the expert knowledge of the American food-processing and distribution industry in a drive to close the protein gap in areas where supplies of animal proteins are inadequate to meet minimum nutritional standards. We know that these efforts will not immediately reach the lowest income groups, who can be helped only by government-subsidized fortification of cereals. We aim to reach the large segment of society that lives at just above the bare survival level and buys its food.

The new program can be generally divided into three phases: (1) a market survey to determine local tastes and food preferences; (2) design of prototype high-protein foods based on the information gained in phase one; and (3) market testing of several prototypes to learn if they are acceptable to consumers. The food products must be manufactured from raw materials that are or can be made available locally, in plentiful supply and at reasonable prices.

AID is financing the first and third phases of this program. The knowledge gained in these phases will be made public and will be available to all food companies with similar objectives. The prototype development phase is financed by a contracting company, which retains all information on its specific product. By mid-1967, five contracts had been signed with U.S. companies to go forward with projects under this program, and several more were being negotiated. Under study are a protein beverage for El Salvador, to appeal to and be within the price range of everyone; a soy protein beverage, fortified corn foods, and soy foods for Brazil—all designed to compete successfully in price and taste appeal with unfortified foods regularly consumed in large volume; and protein-enriched wheat foods for Tunisia. Although it is not universally appreciated, this program to discover and promote new, low-cost protein foods tailored to the nutritional needs and eating habits of billions can be a major technological and industrial effort.

In the summer of 1966, in Hong Kong, I observed one example of what can be done. I met with a Chinese food manufacturer and distributor who had developed a product called Vitasoy—a mildly carbonated drink with a soybean base and a very high protein content. In the Hong Kong schools today, Vitasoy outsells other carbonated drinks with which it competes in price. I tasted it and liked it. A vigorous promotion program bringing this drink to the attention of the school children of Hong Kong has been highly successful. The techniques used were familiar—awards for the strongest boy and the prettiest girl who drank Vitasoy, and radio, television, and newspaper advertising similar to that for soft drinks in the United States. Several American chemical and food companies are now investigating Vitasoy. If their findings are favorable, they may adapt it to other countries and the day may soon come when this drink will be vital ammunition in the assault on protein deficiency in the developing world.

In the endeavor to get protein enrichment to the countries where it is desperately needed, we are witnessing an important cooperative effort between government and private industry. In the long run, the protein gap will be closed in the commercial market, as the fertilizer gap is beginning to be. I am confident that business leaders in the United States and elsewhere in the developed world are interested in enlarging their share of the effort to win the war on hunger. They will invest time, talent, and resources in the developing countries if asked, and if the conditions are reasonable and fair. In the past year, I have met with leading American businessmen on many occasions. I have asked them quite frankly to tell us what conditions would make possible a sharp expansion of their investment abroad. I have assured them that the U.S. Government, at the highest level, would cooperate with them in every way possible to bring about more favorable investment climates. A much deeper involvement of private industry is an absolute necessity in the job of feeding the world's people.

CHAPTER 7

❧

Volunteers and Voluntary Agencies

❧

Volunteers and voluntary agencies play a unique role in technical-assistance programs. The volunteers provide a people-to-people expression of concern, and the agencies can carry out research and other work that would not be undertaken either by the United States or the recipient nations. Because they are free from political ties, both in the United States and in the host countries, these groups can experiment with new types of programs and pave the way for government support of those that are successful. Volunteers and voluntary agencies also bring to people of the United States first-hand insight into the problems and aspirations of other peoples. This relationship helps to establish understanding of an interdependent world and builds support for international development programs.

The Technical Assistance Information Clearing House publishes a directory of 500 nonprofit groups engaged in technical assistance overseas. Their combined expenditures approach $750 million annually. Many of these organizations have been in the aid business longer than the U.S. Government, and have maintained a mutually helpful relationship with official programs.

THE FOUNDATIONS

The numerous foundations that figure so large in American life have provided leadership, technical assistance, and some capital for economic development all over the world—particularly since World War II. They have emphasized research and education, especially in the fields of agriculture and health. They have been an important source of funds for scholarships and fellowships (on the theory that, in the long run, countries will make lasting progress only when they have their own specialists) and for the establishment and support of research and educational institutions in specialized fields and in areas lacking such facilities. They help host countries with pilot projects and demonstration programs. Frequently, two or more foundations will join in support of a project. Foundations also make grants to other voluntary organizations to carry out operations in specialized fields.

The Rockefeller and Ford foundations are two of the largest. The Rockefeller Foundation was established in 1913 "to promote the well-being of mankind throughout the world." Prior to 1941, it had not engaged in agricultural development. By 1940, however, its health workers recognized that nutrition was an important part of health, and that better nutrition required more productive agriculture.

Besides the wealthy philanthropists, other influential Americans, including Henry A. Wallace, Secretary of Agriculture from 1933 to 1940, recognized the problem of undernourishment. Wallace knew that Congress would not approve the use of public funds to help a foreign country grow corn and wheat while the United States had huge surpluses of both. Here was a situation in which a foundation could act where government could not. On February 3, 1941, at a conference in his of-

fice, Wallace, then Vice-President, told representatives of the
Rockefeller Foundation that an increase in the yield per acre
of corn and beans in Mexico could contribute more than anything else to the welfare of the people there.

The Foundation took up the challenge. Corn improvement
received top priority. Corn is used for the daily bread of the
Mexican people, but average yields in Mexico in 1941 were
only about eight bushels an acre. (The average at that time
in the United States was nearly thirty-five bushels, and yields
of 100 bushels were not uncommon.) Corn breeders went
to work to develop a disease-resistant, high-yielding hybrid
suited to Mexican conditions. As soon as a new hybrid showed
superiority, it was released to farmers; meanwhile, research
continued to develop even better ones. In 1948, for the first
time since the revolution of 1910, Mexico had no need to import corn. Once hybrid corn became established on the larger
farms, managed by the more progressive farmers, the expansion slowed down, however. Getting hybrid corn seed into use
by small farmers proved to be a far more difficult, costly, and
time-consuming task than the research to develop suitable
varieties.

The Rockefeller Foundation's research program in wheat
improvement in Mexico has been mentioned earlier. It, too,
was a stunning success. Wheat rust had caused so many crop
failures that many farmers had shifted to other crops, although, on irrigated land, wheat could be the most productive
and profitable. As scientists developed wheat with resistance
to rust and with short, stiff stems that stood erect even with
heavy applications of fertilizer and water, farmers on irrigated
land quickly adopted the new varieties and new practices. The
increases in wheat yields per acre and in total production
made a large contribution to the 7 per cent annual increase
in Mexican food production during the 1950's.

The consequences of these research programs spread world-
wide. Today, research centers in Mexico are training scien-

tists from Asia, Africa, and Latin America. New varieties of Mexican wheat are among the most promising weapons available to India, Pakistan, and Turkey in the fight to feed their people. Additional research centers of the type established in Mexico are being organized in Asia and Africa.

Corn, wheat, and rice are the three major food grains that sustain man. More than one-half of the world's people prefer rice. It grows in warm, humid climates, where it is frequently under irrigation. A rice variety that would mature quickly, respond well to fertilizer, and resist disease would make an immense contribution to the war on hunger. Scientists at the International Rice Research Institute (IRRI) in Los Banos, the Philippines—established in 1962 as a joint undertaking by the Rockefeller Foundation, the Ford Foundation, and the Philippine Government—are striving to develop such a variety.

During 1966, IRRI rice varieties were tested in India, Malaysia, Pakistan, and the Philippines. One variety yielded an average of 80 per cent more than local varieties in all four countries. It is a short-strawed rice that uses the plant nutrients in fertilizer to produce more seed, rather than more stems and leaves. Plant breeders are experimenting with varieties that mature within 120 days of planting, rather than in the usual 150 to 200 days. Such early-maturing varieties could make two, or even three, crops a year. Another factor in increasing the possible number of crops a year is light. Some varieties of rice will not flower and set seed when daylight lasts more than twelve hours. These can be grown only seasonally. Other strains are less sensitive to light, and are being used to develop high-yielding varieties that can be grown at any time of the year.

Training rice scientists is an important part of the IRRI's work. Each rice-growing country needs its own research institutions to find solutions to its individual problems. A total of 104 scholars from nineteen countries received training at the

IRRI in 1966. The Institute also provides technical assistance to other centers in the Philippines, Ceylon, India, Pakistan, Thailand, and Malaysia. The most recent addition to foundation-sponsored international agricultural research institutions is the International Institute of Tropical Research (IITR) at Ibadan, Nigeria. It will undertake research on such foods as corn, soybeans, peanuts, cassava, yams, and grain sorghum, and will provide training for agricultural specialists from many lands.

The Ford Foundation cooperated in the establishment and support of the IRRI and the IITR. In addition, it has also made some important individual contributions. Henry and Edsel Ford started their foundation in 1936. In the beginning, it was relatively small, and made grants mainly in Detroit and in the state of Michigan. In 1949, upon receipt of bequests from the estates of the founders, it became the largest foundation in the world. Its commitment to the establishment of peace and the strengthening of democracy led it to undertake projects overseas.

One of the Ford Foundation's most significant contributions is the support of social science research in politically sensitive fields. In the early 1950's, the research that it financed on programs of technical assistance in Latin America provided our first real evaluation of such work. The Ford Foundation programs in India also began in the early 1950's. Through its contributions of capital and specialists to the Indian community-development program, it seeks to raise the living standards of 375 million rural people. Besides making large contributions to institutions for the training of local leaders, it has helped to establish pilot projects and demonstration areas. In 1959, a team of Ford Foundation experts analyzed India's food problems and made policy recommendations to both the Indian Government and the various outside agencies trying to help India as it became apparent that rural improvement was too slow. Unfortunately, some of the key recommendations were not implemented until famine threatened. Today, the Foundation is supporting an intensive program to provide better seed, fertilizer, insecticides, and technical guidance to areas where prospects are best for large increases in yields and total production.

The foundations have led the way in demographic and population-control research and financial assistance to birth-control programs. Prior to 1960, when neither the U.S. Government nor the international organizations would face these problems, the foundations were supporting them. The Population Council, a foundation established in 1952, fosters research and provides technical assistance. It is deeply involved in the population-control program of Taiwan. The Planned Parenthood Federation of America, the Hugh Moore Fund, the World Population Emergency Campaign, and the International Planned Parenthood Federation are interrelated organizations engaged in public education and action programs. With generous grants from the large foundations, they provide specialists, laboratory equipment, and supplies to countries that request assistance.

Foundations are also helping to finance nutrition research. In an earlier chapter, I discussed the development of new high-protein foods for mass merchandising by private industry. Such development requires research in marketing and merchandising, as well as in food technology. This work is costly, and the risks are high. Even with the U.S. Government underwriting part of the costs, private industry is not moving into this field fast enough to accomplish all that is desirable. The Kellogg Foundation has made a notable contribution through its support of the Central American Institute of Nutrition, which developed and marketed the first of the successful high-protein foods, Incaparina. After this product was proven commercially, its manufacture and distribution were licensed to a private company.

Several regional institutes of food technology are needed to undertake research on the processing of food from local products for local consumption. Special emphasis should be placed on protein sources, and the institutes should carry through the development process by promoting and popularizing the new products. Research should also be focused on simple techniques adapted for small businesses in villages or small towns, where much food is wasted for lack of processing or storage. The foundations could support such institutes.

PRIVATELY SPONSORED ORGANIZATIONS

Many organizations engaged in technical-assistance and food-distribution programs, such as religious groups, depend upon private sponsors for support. The U.S. Government gives some food and helps pay for shipping donated goods, but the major costs are paid for by the contributions of millions of interested Americans. The Department of State's Advisory Committee on Voluntary Foreign Aid lists sixty-seven voluntary agencies eligible to receive direct financial assistance from the U.S. Government. In 1966, AID paid $5.5 million to ship about $65 million in privately donated supplies sent overseas by registered organizations, including the Church World Service, Catholic Relief Services, the American Jewish Joint Distribution Committee, and the Cooperative for American Relief Everywhere (CARE).

Registered agencies are also eligible to receive American agricultural commodities under the P.L. 480 Food for Freedom program. In 1966, these organizations carried out food-distribution programs, including food for work and school lunch programs, which reached 72 million persons—half of them children. Registered voluntary agencies may also purchase excess government property—such as tools, vehicles, medical instruments, and laboratory equipment—at 15 per cent of the original cost. AID pays ocean transportation costs on this food and equipment for overseas use.

The requirements for registration stipulate that an agency must have an active board of directors, a continuing program overseas, purposes other than political or propagandistic, records indicating financial stability, and proof that contributions to it are tax deductible. The registered agencies are private independent groups supported by the free gifts of the American people.

Almost all of the registered agencies are engaged in food distribution on a scale that would be beyond their means without the donated food available from the U.S. Government. The voluntary agency supervises or assists the local government in food distribution, trains local personnel, and contributes funds for equipment, supplemental foods, and other necessary supplies. Major emphasis has been placed on school lunch and maternal- and child-feeding programs. In some countries, the voluntary agencies have successfully worked themselves out of a job by demonstrating the feasibility and effectiveness of child nutrition programs.

The second major food-distribution program carried out by voluntary agencies has been the relief of disaster victims. CARE is the largest operator in this work. This widely known organization was set up in 1945. Through it, Americans could send relief packages of food and textiles to war-torn Europe. Since that time, CARE has sent food packages carefully selected to meet diet deficiencies and local food habits to people in all parts of the world. Most of the food is donated by the U.S. Government under the Food for Peace program, which enables CARE to send a ten-pound package of food at a cost of only $1. CARE also provides seeds and tools to contribute to the solution of farm production problems. CARE does a good deal of long-range planning, and its work is closely coordinated with local technical-assistance and welfare programs.

The CARE program in the famine-struck state of Bihar, in India, during 1966–67, used about 8 million pounds of milk powder a month to feed each of 5 million children eight ounces of fluid milk a day. According to an Indian report, even this vast effort reached barely 25 per cent of the children in the state. Other voluntary agencies operated free kitch ens and food-for-work programs. The activities of such religious groups as the Catholic Relief Service and the National Christian Council's Committee for Relief and Gift Supplies (CORAGS) were singled out for special praise by B. G. Verghese, press secretary to Prime Minister Indira Gandhi. Mr. Verghese wrote:

The food-for-work programme organized by the Catholic Relief Service, CORAGS, and (through the latter) the Samanvaya Ashram in Bodh Gaya, and some others, constitute a superior method of relief. Here, individual members of a family work on wells, banks or roads and receive in wages as much grain as will feed the family. . . . The food-for-work rates are much more attractive since the grain is assured on site. However, more than the wage-rate, the programme is to be lauded for the excellent results it has achieved: the creation of valuable permanent assets, a spirit of self-help and community participation. . . . However, the real point is that very often Christian missionaries have been the only source of medical care, education and general assistance and comfort to remote backward and neglected tribal communities for years. They are there this year, and they will be there next year and the year after. These people are "friends"; most of the others who have come to give Relief this year are "strangers"; even politicians.

The religious groups and some of the other voluntary agencies have had many years' experience in providing medical, educational, housing, rural development, and agricultural services. All of them believe in self-help. (The Near East Foundation based its programs of rehabilitation after World War I on this principle.) The U.S. Protestant churches alone now have in service abroad more than 500 professionally trained workers in agriculture, home economics and nutrition, extension work, rural sociology, and cooperatives. A decade ago, representatives of religious agencies engaged in technical assistance abroad outnumbered those from the U.S. Government. Most missionary activity in establishing schools and health institutions has ended, because government organizations are undertaking these responsibilities. But in agriculture the need is still acute. The Department of Agriculture offers training in foreign agricultural development for rural missionaries of all denominations, and my colleagues tell me that these workers are among the most dedicated of the many people who come to the Department for such instruction. As long ago as 1944, the Federal Extension Service initiated an annual seminar on extension education for missionaries. Several land-grant colleges, following the lead of Cornell University, offer annual short courses in agricultural techniques. In addition, a considerable number of regular agricultural students in the colleges become missionaries.

COOPERATIVES AND OTHERS

Agricultural cooperatives engaged in foreign programs constitute a special type of voluntary organization whose mission is to build organizations like their own in other countries. They represent a highly developed form of self-help. Cooperatives cultivate the skills needed to build free societies —democratic organization, member participation in decision-making, training in leadership, and self-reliance.

Some co-op groups pioneered in overseas development of credit institutions for farmers and workingmen. The Credit Union National Association (CUNA International), for example, has been providing technical assistance in developing credit unions for many years. The Cooperative League helped to organize cooperatives in India during the 1950's. The Humphrey Amendment to the Foreign Assistance Act of 1961, sponsored by then Senator Hubert H. Humphrey, of Minnesota, directed AID to use the resources of cooperatives, credit unions, and savings and loan associations in foreign aid. Through contractual agreements with AID, people who helped to build our own cooperatives are working overseas to create organizations that provide credit to small farmers, extend electricity to rural areas, build low-cost housing, and organize group marketing and purchasing. American cooperative advisers are helping countries to establish a solid legal basis for their cooperatives and are training leaders here and abroad for cooperative work.

The Department of Agriculture has a close working partnership with AID and the cooperatives in this endeavor, because for forty years it has had a mandate from Congress to provide specific help to cooperatives in the United States. The Department of Agriculture is providing cooperative advisers to foreign governments, and educational materials and special assistance to all cooperative specialists overseas. These are but beginnings. We must give more help to cooperatives in the early stages if their members are to accomplish in fifteen years what it took us 100 years to do. The leaders of the new cooperatives in Africa, Asia, and Latin America need ready access to the experience of older cooperative organizations. We do not have enough knowledgeable men located in strategic places around the world to fill this need—and will not be using our foreign-aid funds wisely if we fail to provide the development loans and technical assistance to sustain the cooperative movement.

There are so many different types of voluntary organizations engaged in technical assistance that any American can find a place to make a contribution. For example, Self-Help, Inc., started by a Waverly, Iowa, farmer and industrialist in 1950, is hard at work repairing usable farm equipment and moving it to needy farmers abroad at a reasonable cost. There is enough outdated equipment rusting away on American farms to keep volunteer repair men busy for decades. Future Farmers of America, a youth organization in rural high schools, is helping in some areas. Such youth groups need skilled adult leadership and funds for tools and repair parts.

Americans, surrounded by the most advanced technology in history, cannot even imagine how difficult it may be to find the simplest kind of information in a developing country. To assist in this problem, Volunteers for International Technical Assistance (VITA), a nonprofit information clearing-house, has 4,500 technically skilled volunteers who answer inquiries from people living in the developing nations. Besides its inquiry service, VITA has a research and development program to mobilize assistance on technical problems. For example, a VITA volunteer developed a design for a cooking stove that uses solar heat. It can be built inexpensively out of local materials. Since some parts of the world are so short on fuel that the land has been stripped of vegetation so that animal dung is being used for fuel, the widespread use of such a cooker could, in time, contribute to soil conservation, to increasing the supply of organic fertilizer, and, ultimately, to the production of more food.

The most exciting new dimension in technical assistance in the 1960's is the Peace Corps. A happy combination of voluntary workers and government financial and organizational support, the Peace Corps has many of the best attributes of voluntary organizations. Peace Corps workers are very carefully selected and thoroughly trained before being sent out. Since they are all volunteers and are told from the beginning not to expect to maintain an "American" standard of living in their overseas posts, they have a sense of dedication not always felt by American civil servants on overseas assignments. They work at the grass roots, rather than at the administrative level—and they work directly with ordinary people, frequently engaging in manual labor, which is still scorned by the elite of government and professional circles in the developing countries. In many instances, the Peace Corps man or woman is able to gain a degree of acceptance by the ordinary people, a confidence denied to others. One African, for example, said that there were three kinds of people in his country—Africans, Europeans, and Peace Corps members. The term of service is usually two years. Although this short term circumvents accusations of Peace Corpsmen being colonists in disguise, it also, unfortunately, limits their effectiveness.

The Peace Corps recognizes community development as one of its principal areas of operation. Since problems of community development and food production are usually closely associated in rural areas, the Peace Corps volunteer frequently finds himself grappling with problems of low productivity, low prices for salable surpluses, inadequate storage and marketing facilities, and production items like seed, fertilizer, and insecticides being either not available or priced beyond the means of producers.

Peace Corps volunteers assigned to rural areas need training in agrculture. They also need extensive backstopping by the extension services and agricultural colleges of the host country, as well as by agricultural institutions in the United States. The Department of Agriculture is prepared to furnish this backstopping, and the land-grant colleges have demonstrated that they are willing and able to help. The Peace Corps realizes that better training in, and more emphasis on, agriculture are important in the future, and I am confident that its volunteers will play an increasingly important role in winning the war on hunger.

A PATRIOTIC SERVICE

Despite all the accomplishments of voluntary agencies, qualified volunteers of every kind, in sufficient number, and adequate funds for their work are still needed. For several years, AID, the Department of Agriculture, and several land-grant colleges have been recruiting agricultural scientists and technicians for service overseas, but many positions remain unfilled because of lack of qualified applicants. The Peace Corps is trying to recruit people with farm backgrounds or training in agriculture, but they are getting only a trickle of volunteers, although many, including women and older men, could serve in this capacity. All of us must realize that volunteers, whether they be salaried professionals or propertyless monks, have made and continue to make important contributions to the war on hunger. To join their ranks or to give them support—financial or otherwise—is a deed of patriotism.

❦

International Cooperation

❦

In previous chapters, I have emphasized that the task of preventing a world-wide food crisis is much too large for any one
country. It is a job for all.

A program to improve maize (corn) production in Kenya
shows what can be accomplished through international cooperation. This joint effort is sponsored by the Kenyan Government, Great Britain's Ministry of Overseas Development,
the Rockefeller Foundation, and the Agricultural Research
Service of the U.S. Department of Agriculture. Its purpose is
to increase the yield of maize through a combination of research and education.

Work began in 1958, and the United States became active
in 1963. The first experimental work was to determine which
factors most influenced maize yields in Kenya, where the best
lands for maize are found at high altitudes and have long, wet
seasons. The experiments showed that the time of planting
and the type of maize were the most important, followed by
the number of plants per acre, weed control, and fertilization.
The next step was to develop hybrids, starting with a hardy

local variety. The scientists decided that a lack of genetic diversity in maize grown locally was limiting productivity, so new strains were brought in from the United States, Mexico, and Latin America. The move was successful, and by 1966 one hybrid was yielding seventy-one bushels per acre, compared with an average of thirteen bushels per acre before the breeding work began.

As part of an extension program, thousands of demonstration plots on small holdings were established where people could see the results. The cooperators bought their own hybrid seed and fertilizer and followed cultural practices recommended by the agricultural advisers. When hybrid maize seed was first offered for sale in 1963, Kenyan farmers planted about 400 acres. Each year thereafter, they increased the acreage planted with hybrids as fast as the new seed became available. In 1967, for the first time, there was seed for all who wanted it. About 300,000 acres were planted with hybrid maize, with two-thirds of the acreage grown by small farmers. Yields averaged about seventy bushels per acre, and, almost overnight, Kenya became a corn-exporting nation.

The groups concerned and the Kenyan farmers together have demonstrated what can be done through international cooperation in bringing agricultural research to Kenya and applying it to local conditions. Here lies our hope for the future. Our experience in Kenya convinces me that the mobilization of skilled manpower from the developed countries is a field in which international organizations, particularly the United Nations and its specialized agencies, can make a great contribution.

Programs of the United Nations and Its Specialized Agencies

Most of what we read and hear about the United Nations relates to the activities of the General Assembly and the Security Council. The Security Council is concerned primarily with peace-keeping problems. The peace-building activities of the United Nations are not so well publicized. These activities are carried on under the Economic and Social Council and the specialized agencies, such as the Food and Agricultural Organization (FAO).

The Economic and Social Council serves as a forum for the discussion of development problems and proposals to deal with them. If the members of the Council are able to come to an agreement, it is embodied in a resolution, passed by the Council, and sent to the General Assembly for appropriate action. For example, the General Assembly, on November 21, 1963, unanimously adopted a resolution proclaiming 1965 as International Cooperation Year. The purpose was to focus world attention on what President Johnson called "the assignment of the century" and "a clear necessity to our survival." During the year, each nation conducted a review of the progress made in international cooperation and its contributions—past and future—to the endeavor. An intensive effort was undertaken to make the people of the various countries more aware of peace-building through international cooperation.

Within the Economic and Social Council are a number of functional and regional commissions. Most of them hold biannual meetings, at which country representatives discuss problems and possible solutions. Proposals originating in these commissions are often brought before the Economic and Social Council for action. The regional economic commissions have been particularly effective in stimulating regional projects, such as development banks. The Economic Commission for Asia and the Far East has strongly supported plans for international cooperation in the development of the Mekong River Basin. This project has been funded by a consortium, in which a group of nations have pledged contributions, under the supervision of the World Bank. The Latin

American Economic Commission sponsored the Latin American Free Trade Area and the Central American Common Market. The Economic Commission for Europe spans the Iron Curtain. Although it mirrors most of the differences between East and West, and therefore seldom reaches consensus, it may serve for future bridge-building.

A resolution of the Economic and Social Council of the United Nations initiated the Expanded Technical Assistance Program in 1949, in response to President Truman's inaugural address inviting all countries to pool their technological resources for the improvement of underdeveloped areas. Called "expanded" because it was in addition to those already being carried out by the U.N. specialized agencies, this program provides specialists and technicians for a large number of relatively small projects. Very little money is provided for supplies and equipment.

The obvious need for a program that could supply equipment as well as personnel for certain types of projects led to the establishment in 1959 of the United Nations Special Fund. Its job is to carry out fairly large preinvestment projects, which will lay the groundwork for future investments from either public or private sources. Examples of Special Fund projects include natural resource surveys and training schools to develop the technical, managerial, and executive skills needed by industry.

Both of these programs have received financial support from voluntary contributions made by the participating national governments at an annual pledging conference. The regular U.N. budget is separate and is met by assessments on member nations according to a predetermined formula. By December 31, 1966, the Special Fund had financed 657 preinvestment studies. The flow of capital arising from projects begun as the result of only 31 of these studies totals more than $1.6 billion. Approximately 11,000 persons attended courses offered by 378 training centers assisted by the Special Fund.

On November 22, 1965, the U.N. General Assembly adopted a resolution that consolidated the Expanded Technical Assistance Program and the Special Fund into a U.N. Development Program. By mid-1967, the Governing Council of the Development Program had assigned 308 of a total of 778 Special Fund projects to the FAO. A significant additional number of projects assigned to other agencies were in areas closely related to food, such as transportation, basic literacy, and population research. In November, 1966, the Council approved a two-year technical-assistance program totaling $110.7 million, with most of the money scheduled to support 6,000 experts in the field, and 25 per cent going for agricultural projects. Education and public health each received 15 per cent.

Although this is the largest addition to the U.N. program of assistance to developing countries in any year to date, both the Secretary-General of the United Nations and the Administrator of the Development Program have warned that significant further increases will be necessary if the objectives of the development decade are to be met by 1970. Although contributions have been rising slowly, they have not climbed as fast as the national incomes of the donor countries. The countries of the U.N. family must, according to Secretary-General U Thant, "be willing to follow up declarations of intent by the actual implementation of specific programmes and policies, many of which will involve some sacrifice."

The U.N. Children's Fund (UNICEF) is another source of technical assistance. It was established by the General Assembly in December, 1946, with funds remaining after the dissolution of the U.N. Relief and Rehabilitation Administration (UNRRA). Its support comes from voluntary contributions by government, private organizations, and individuals. Projects aimed at improving the nutrition of children and pregnant and nursing women are among its many activities.

The technical-assistance programs are carried out mostly by

the so-called specialized agencies, each of which was set up because a number of countries felt the need to cooperate in a
given field. Relatively independent, each specialized agency
has its own separate budget, governing body, constitution, and
member nations. Memberships overlap, but are not identical
among the agencies or with the membership of the United Nations. Three of the largest and most powerful, the FAO, the
World Health Organization (WHO), and the U.N. Educational, Scientific, and Cultural Organization (UNESCO), are
concerned with food and population problems.

The FAO was established in October, 1945, and now has a
membership of 116 nations. Its principal functions are to serve
its member governments as an agricultural information clearinghouse and to give technical advice in the fields of agriculture, fisheries, forestry, nutrition, and home economics. In its
early years, the FAO concentrated on gathering and diffusing
information and sponsoring international meetings, at which
people could exchange information and discuss problems. Its
technical-assistance activities grew slowly until the advent of
the Expanded Technical Assistance Program. A further expansion took place with the assignment to the FAO of many
U.N. Special Fund projects.

The FAO is now carrying out over 200 projects for the
U.N. development program, employing about 1,250 experts.
Among their various activities, these specialists are helping
to fight animal disease in Africa, where many epidemics orig-
inate. They are successfully controlling the desert locust—a
pest that has destroyed man's food supply since Biblical times.
They are helping to locate underground water supplies in
Saudi Arabia, assisting in the construction of grain-storage
facilities in Somalia, and helping to develop food-storage,
processing, and marketing facilities in Malaysia.

The growing world food crisis led to the inauguration by
the FAO on July 1, 1960, of a five-year Freedom from Hunger
Campaign, which sought to increase public awareness of the

world food problem and to stimulate support for food programs from private as well as public agencies. Among the activities of the Freedom from Hunger Campaign was the $1 million World Fertilizer Program, financed by several hundred fertilizer companies in North America, Europe, and Japan. In 1966, this program was extended for three years. It has held more than 88,000 demonstrations in twenty-three countries. Another project, sponsored by the Norwegian Church Relief Fund, sent five Norwegian farm families to live in eastern Nigeria to demonstrate how to grow better crops, raise healthier livestock, and purify the water supply. The 1965 FAO Conference decided to continue the Freedom from Hunger Campaign for an additional five years.

The FAO also administers the World Food Program. The United Nations, again following an idea originated by the United States, began, in 1962, a three-year experimental program to use food from countries with surpluses to promote economic growth in developing countries. Seventy countries made contributions of $100 million in food, cash, and services. Among the 115 projects in fifteen countries was the financing of the relocation of 50,000 Sudanese farmers and their families, moved from the area being flooded by the Aswan High Dam. Many children in Nepal have benefited from the use of over 100 tons of dry skim milk, which was combined with locally produced buffalo milk to make it more digestible and to increase the quantity of milk available. Proceeds from the sale of the milk were used to build ten additional milk-collecting stations and a new chilling center. Forestry projects in Turkey, Lebanon, and Sudan; watershed improvement in Jamaica; and land reclamation in Taiwan and the Republic of Chad are other examples of development projects in which food was used as pay for the workers.

The United Nations and the FAO have endorsed the continuation and expansion of the World Food Program for as long as multilateral food aid is found feasible and desirable.

The goal of the program for the second three-year period is $275 million in food and cash, an increase of $175 million over the goal for the initial three-year period.

The FAO is now engaged in the mammoth task of preparing an "Indicative World Plan for Agricultural Development." On a country-by-country and region-by-region basis, it is surveying needs and priorities for the next two decades and hopes to place a first version of the plan before the Second World Food Conference, to be held in Europe in the summer of 1968. When the cost of this immense and complicated undertaking proved beyond the resources of the FAO, it appealed to private foundations and other bodies concerned with fostering economic growth to provide $2.5 million in supplementary funds.

In September, 1948, the WHO formally came into existence. It is concerned with all aspects of human health. One of the large areas in which it operates is the control and eventual elimination of epidemic diseases, which affect millions of people on many continents. Malaria is a case in point. Before World War II, malaria had been virtually eradicated in the developed countries. When allied soldiers in large numbers came down with the disease in Malta and Egypt, antimalaria campaigns were successfully mounted in those areas. After the war, it seemed intolerable that mankind should continue to suffer this scourge, and, under WHO leadership, areas encompassing more than 800 million people have been freed of malaria. Nevertheless, nearly half of the malarious areas of the world need additional help to eradicate the disease.

Among the long-range health problems being tackled by WHO is the provision of adequate supplies of pure water, since polluted water is the source of many deadly or debilitating diseases and a serious obstacle to economic development. In cooperation with the FAO and UNICEF, WHO is concerned with nutrition and pure food supplies. The modern science of nutrition was pioneered by research begun by the

U.S. Department of Agriculture in 1894. The cumulative results of this research by the Department and the state agricultural experiment stations enabled the Department, during
World War II, to provide data on nutrition requirements
translated into food-production requirements. As food shortages developed, allocation of the available food supply among
the allied powers was also based on nutrition research by the
Department, and its wartime cooperation with the British
Food Mission set the stage for postwar international cooperation on world nutrition problems. Department of Agriculture
research in nutrition and food processing is coordinated with
similar research and programs of the international organizations. The nutrition work of these organizations is directed
toward the most effective use of available foodstuffs and the
development of new high-quality foods at prices that people
can afford.

Three-fourths of the world's milk is produced in Europe,
North America, and Australia. In tropical climates, cattle are
highly subject to disease, and careful sanitation in the collection and processing of milk is essential if it is to reach consumers in a wholesome condition. Most of the developing
countries could improve their dairy production, and their
governments are investing important resources in this effort.
The FAO has provided technical assistance in dairy husbandry to many governments; UNICEF has concentrated on
providing assistance in the industrial processing of milk.

In recent years, as discussed elsewhere in these pages, an
increasing amount of attention has been focused on the development of new high-protein foods, especially those suitable
for children. The cheapest source of animal protein is fish,
but it is usually available only in coastal areas. People living
as little as fifty miles from the sea may never have seen or
eaten fish. A cheap, virtually tasteless and odorless high-protein powder made from fish would provide an ideal supple-

ment for upgrading the protein value of foods on which infants are traditionally weaned in many areas.

Both the FAO and UNICEF are rapidly expanding their work in developing fisheries and fish products. A fish-flour plant with a capacity of 300 tons a year has been built at Quintero, Chile, with UNICEF assistance. The FAO has already helped to bring about major changes in the fishing industry in Southeast Asia through the introduction of small, powered fishing boats of modern design. By changing from traditional equipment to one of these new boats, a typical fisherman might increase his daily catch from fifteen pounds to 400 pounds. World fish production doubled between 1953 and 1963. This and projected future increases in production have focused attention on the need for a coordinated international program on fishing and fisheries—emphasizing conservation and replenishment of supplies, as well as improvement of harvesting techniques.

The U.N. agencies have also given high priority to the development of palatable protein foods from oilseed crops. A vegetable milk powder, for example, is now being produced in Indonesia in a plant built with UNICEF assistance, and UNICEF has also supplied equipment for two peanut-flour plants in India. In these and related efforts, our Agricultural Research Service is working closely with scientists from developing countries selected by UNICEF. The scientists are devising ways to process high-protein flours and use them in preparing foods acceptable to local tastes. Small machines for home or community use have been developed for the production of oilseed flours. A hand process being tested requires only time, human muscle, an open fire—and an open mind.

The recent success in the United States in breeding high-lysine corn may revolutionize corn production around the world. Lysine is one of the amino acids (the building blocks from which protein is made) essential to human nutrition.

Corn breeders have discovered a type of corn with a high-lysine content and are now working at top speed to transfer this genetic character to commercial hybrids. Parent stocks of the high-lysine corn have been sent to more than twenty countries, where they are being crossed with locally adapted strains to produce high-yielding hybrids for each area. Plant breeders of the United States and many other parts of the world are now actively seeking genes that will similarly improve the quality of protein in wheat, rice, and other grains. The task is enormous, as thousands of individual plants must be analyzed for lysine content. Success in this undertaking would be one of the greatest boons to man ever recorded.

The international organizations recognize that increasing and improving food supplies is only half the battle. Like the United States, they are changing their attitudes toward population control. When India asked for technical aid from WHO in 1952, the resulting divergence of opinion threatened to split the organization. No assistance was given. By contrast, in December, 1963, two other U.N. units—the Economic Commission for Asia and the Far East and the Social Affairs Department—sponsored the first Asian Population Conference. The governments and agencies represented passed a resolution calling on the United Nations to expand the scope of technical assistance available to governments to include family-welfare planning programs, stressing the existence in Asia of greatly reduced mortality without corresponding declines in fertility.

In 1965, after a bitter fight, WHO passed a resolution to provide assistance to its members in developing population policy, but not to participate in direct operations. A similar resolution was adopted by the Economic and Social Council of the United Nations. It is desirable that this very sensitive subject be handled by international organizations, as well as through bilateral technical-assistance programs. In particular, WHO can take a leading role in helping countries that desire assistance with family planning.

When UNESCO was established late in 1945, its activities were confined largely to promoting the exchange of scientific information through international meetings, fellowships, scholarships, and exchange professorships. It also promoted the building of libraries and archives through exchanges and translations, and the cataloging of existing information. The development of a body of research on the prevalence of illiteracy and the close correlation between illiteracy and poverty has led to a growing emphasis on education at the lower levels. Under the Expanded Technical Assistance Program, UNESCO is sending teams of experts to developing countries, particularly newly independent countries, to help organize school systems. These educational programs, in time, will have great impact on agricultural programs.

The world-wide responsibilities and operations of the United Nations in the food, agriculture, health, and population fields would lead one to expect a vast expenditure of funds; however, the regular annual budget of the United Nations amounts to a little over $100 million, that of the FAO to about $30 million, and that of WHO to about $40 million. The agency budgets are assessed on the member countries according to a formula based upon the wealth of each country. The assessment of the United States is about 32 per cent of the total. When compared with the U.S. Government budget, U.N. expenditures seem small indeed. For example, our AID budget in recent years has been approximately $2 billion annually. The services of the Department of Agriculture to farmers, consumers, and business cost about $7 billion annually. And our military expenditures (exclusive of special appropriations for the conduct of the war in Viet-Nam) amount to nearly $50 billion.

The U.N. technical-assistance fund, small though it is,

must be divided among hundreds of claimants. Each developing country wants its share, and each specialized agency promotes projects it has found to be most worthwhile. Consequently, the size of projects tends to be small. Capital for them must come from other sources. Although U.N. multilateral assistance forms a minor part of the total flow of aid to developing countries, its contributions are vital. Many of these countries have only recently achieved independence and are extremely sensitive about anything that might, even remotely, appear to be political or economic domination or interference in their internal affairs. The United Nations has made provision to meet the needs of young and inexperienced governments for operational, executive, and administrative personnel under what is called the OPEX program. Experts are provided to governments as their temporary employees, generally at the higher levels of government departments and institutions. The OPEX personnel are expected to train replacements for themselves while carrying out their regular duties.

Where agricultural development programs impinge on the vested interests of the political elite—as, for example, in the breaking up of large landholdings or the revision of tax systems—these important citizens of the developing countries can accept the advice of and the pressure exerted by an international body more gracefully than that of a rich and powerful nation. Consequently, even a small U.N. technical-assistance program may supply the ingredient that determines the success or failure of a large bilateral aid program. There is room and, indeed, need for a great expansion in this type of technical assistance by the United Nations.

In an ideal world, perhaps the ideal way of carrying out technical assistance would be to channel all of it through the United Nations. If the United States were to channel all of its aid through the United Nations, however, the necessity for our concurrence in plans for using these funds would deprive that agency of its independence and, consequently, of much of its usefulness. The United States has used its influence to get the United Nations and its specialized agencies to increase their regular budgets. The regular budget of the FAO, for example, has been increased from $9.2 million in 1960 to almost $30 million in 1968. Even more notable are the increases for development-assistance programs financed by contributed funds. Expenditures increased from $10.8 million in 1960 to $52.9 million in 1967.

THE ORGANIZATION FOR ECONOMIC COOPERATION AND DEVELOPMENT

Not all international cooperation is within the United Nations. The Communist-bloc and the non-Communist countries each have their own international organizations. For the developed nations of the West, the Organization for Economic Cooperation and Development (OECD), mentioned earlier, is extremely important. This organization has broad objectives, recognizing that the policies of the developed countries have a particularly strong influence on the developing countries. It seeks to promote sound economic expansion of the world economy. Member countries of the OECD provide the lion's share of development aid, both bilateral and multilateral.

The Development Assistance Committee (DAC) of the OECD is endeavoring to promote closer coordination of aid programs at country and regional levels. It is encouraging the aid-giving countries to improve the policies and operations of their assistance programs. It is investigating the forces restricting foreign private investment, in the hope of securing the removal of some of the impediments and promoting the flow of private capital, management, and technical skills into developing countries. The OECD also conducts its own small, multilateral technical-assistance program for developing member and associated countries.

The fifteen governments that are now members of the DAC provided, in one way or another, about $6 billion of aid to the developing countries in 1966. The private sector in these countries added another $3.5 billion and the multilateral agencies, with funds obtained largely from these same countries, disbursed more than $500 million. Additional assistance came from voluntary agencies and foundations in these countries. The DAC has continuously placed great emphasis on increasing the volume of assistance. All experts agree that the amount that could be usefully absorbed by the more than eighty developing countries is much greater than the total available from all sources.

Since, however, the DAC has had only limited success in persuading member countries to increase their assistance, it has recently focused efforts on making what is available more effective. Perhaps the greatest shift in emphasis has been the increasing recognition of agriculture. Another area where new emphasis is evident is that of family planning. The OECD development center is now preparing a report on the potential contributions of DAC countries to population stabilization. A third problem—that of finding enough qualified people to staff technical-assistance programs at all levels—is now receiving attention in the DAC. A fourth problem—and a serious one—is that of debt-servicing. This problem is aggravated by the fact that an increasing proportion of total aid is in the form of loans, rather than grants. The loan proportion of governmental help increased from 24 per cent in 1963 to 36 per cent in 1966. If present trends continue, loans may increase to 60 per cent of all aid within the next five years. The "softness" or "hardness" of the terms under which loans are made may well determine the success or failure of development programs.

The developing countries are in the same position as a family that buys on installment. If the family continues to buy more than it is able to pay for, after a few years such a large proportion of the family income goes to meet installment payments that there is not enough left for food and other daily living costs. High interest rates aggravate the problem and hasten the day of reckoning. The DAC is trying to persuade member countries to allow low interest rates and a generous period for repayment.

THE ALLIANCE FOR PROGRESS

The Organization of American States (OAS) and its development program, the Alliance for Progress, are the product of nearly a century and a half of Western Hemisphere cooperation. When the OAS was chartered in 1948, it absorbed its predecessor, the Pan American Union. The Alliance for Progress is a ten-year development program stressing self-help and internal reforms by the participating nations. It was proposed by President Kennedy in his inaugural address, on January 20, 1961, and adopted by the OAS as the Charter of Punta del Este, on August 17, 1961.

Another hemispheric meeting of chiefs of state was held at Punta del Este, Uruguay, in April, 1967, to review progress under the Charter of 1961. There, President Johnson called for renewed efforts, saying that the next ten years might be declared the decade of urgency. He urged more multinational projects and pledged expanded support by the United States to increase agricultural productivity, as well as to meet other needs. The chiefs of state renewed their commitment to modernize agriculture.

The agricultural goals of the Alliance for Progress are to decrease dependence on exports of raw materials as a source of foreign exchange, to increase productivity, to improve marketing of agricultural products, and to encourage comprehensive agrarian-reform programs that would eliminate extremely small holdings. The countries of Latin America agreed to formulate national development programs and to devote a steadily increasing share of their own resources to the task of meeting their goals.

In compliance with their commitment under the Alliance for Progress, fifteen Latin American countries quickly enacted agrarian-reform laws. Only limited progress has been made to date, however. One of the basic barriers to agricultural development in Latin America is that the great mass of farmers operate minuscule holdings, while some large landowners make minimal use of their land for agricultural production. In a typical area in the Andes, a large hacienda may be found using the fertile valley land for grazing cattle, while the peons cultivate small patches of corn and beans in the poor soil of the adjacent hillsides. Progress is impossible under such conditions. United States aid must be contingent upon these countries' making the necessary changes in land ownership.

The United States has been trying to encourage agricultural development in Latin America for twenty-five years—and many of the lessons we have learned about the success or failure of development schemes have been learned in Latin America. Early efforts were largely on a project basis—an experiment station here, an irrigation program there, and a supervised credit program somewhere else. Frequently, slow initial progress led to disillusionment and early abandonment of the project. Gradually, it has been realized that certain widely prevalent factors adversely affect agricultural development in Latin America. These conditions are the primary targets of the Alliance for Progress.

The inadequacy of information and knowledge—social and economic, as well as technical—is one such problem. Information about production and distribution, soil types and land use, and plant pests and animal diseases is inadequate. Nor are there enough trained people to develop such information.

There are not even enough trainable people to staff the existing training facilities. Educational institutions are located largely in urban centers, and qualified urban youth seek training for the professions, which confer higher social status than farming. Rural youth lack the basic education to qualify for technical agricultural schools. For this reason, much of the technical and capital assistance dispensed through the Alliance for Progress is going into the various facilities and programs of the Inter-American Institute of Agricultural Science.

The Institute, established in 1944 largely as a result of promotion by Secretary of Agriculture Henry A. Wallace, has served as a postgraduate training and research center for the American tropics for nearly twenty years. Now, the Alliance for Progress has assigned it the larger role of encouraging and advancing the agricultural sciences through research, teaching, and extension. Specialized regional training centers are being established in countries of the temperate zone, as well as in those of the tropics. The Institute is supervising research in various national universities; it is also carrying on projects for the collection of basic data in several countries. Research and data collection is a cumulative process. Many developed countries have statistical series that go back 100 years. Geological and cadastral (boundary) surveys of the United States have been in progress for half a century. Modern technology can greatly reduce the time necessary for the collection of basic data, but the task will still take many years.

IN PERSPECTIVE

When regarded in historical perspective, the achievements of the international organizations in the past two decades are truly remarkable. They are blazing new trails and opening clearings in the heart of jungles—literally as well as figuratively.

Today, with their help, we are developing an entirely new body of international law and custom. Only too visibly, our world is shrinking, and we have been forced to a sometimes grudging admission that the technologically advanced countries have a responsibility to help the less developed ones. Now, in the best spirit of international cooperation, we must go on to the larger and optimistic view that the welfare and human dignity of all people contribute to the fulfillment of each of us. And we must remember this above all:

Hungry people have neither well-being nor dignity.

❦

The Food Crisis in India

❦

Almost everything said so far in this book comes into sharp focus on India—the mistakes, the frustrations, the success stories, the magnitude of the task, and the big question: Will India show sufficient determination to help itself to justify continued large-scale assistance from the United States?

There is much to be learned from India's experience. This nation of over 500 million people has been by far the largest recipient of food aid from the United States, even though per capita grants to some other nations have been larger. After neglecting agricultural development for several years, India has recently begun to react to the stark necessity of increasing food production and is now evolving a significant self-help effort.

At the end of 1967, India was recovering from a severe food crisis that threatened the survival of millions of people and the success of the largest experiment in democratic government among the developing nations. The crisis was brought on by two widespread droughts—in the 1965–66 and 1966–67 crop seasons. The first drought was more severe and widespread than those that turned the Great Plains of the United States into a dust bowl during the 1930's. The second one was almost as bad.

These disastrous droughts, coming one after another, called attention to the fact that agricultural production in India had been falling dangerously behind the projected targets of the planners. Population had been increasing at a faster rate than food production. Food shipments from the United States prevented starvation, but they could not solve indefinitely the basic problem of too many people for too little food. In a country where population has been increasing by about 12 million people a year, total food grain production has remained fairly static and the availability of food per person has declined.

Lagging Agricultural Development

India made good progress during the 1950's. Food grain production increased from 55 million metric tons in 1950–51 to 82 million metric tons in 1960–61. During the same period, per capita food grain production increased from 164 to 193 kilograms. Much of this increased production came from expanding existing cultivated areas. But, in recent years, the possibility of opening up new areas has become increasingly limited; most of the productive land is already in cultivation. Thus, there has not been a compensating increase in yields of grain per acre. As a result the 1960's have so far seen a decline in per capita grain production, despite the large increases—5 per cent annually—called for in India's Third Five-Year Plan.* Total food grain production for the first three years of

* In the early 1950's, India decided to industrialize and to raise its standard of living with the aid of a series of so-called five-year plans for economic development. All available resources were to be mobilized and allocated to specific purposes. Numerical targets for increases in production or services were adopted for different segments of the economy, such as agriculture, heavy in-

the plan, 1961–62 to 1963–64, remained more or less constant. Extremely favorable weather conditions brought the production up from 80 million metric tons in 1963–64 to 89 million metric tons in 1964–65. But the drought of 1965–66 brought production down to about 72 million metric tons, requiring India to import over 10 million metric tons of food grains (see Table 3). The second years of drought resulted in food grain production of only 76 million metric tons. Imports of 8.9 million metric tons—mostly from the United States under the Public Law 480 program—were not enough to prevent sharp declines in the amount of grain available for each person.

Even if there had been normal monsoons in India in 1965–66 and 1966–67, there would still have been a serious food shortage. The failure of the monsoons accelerated shortage into crisis. And in the good harvest of 1967–68, with a record food grain crop exceeding 95 million metric tons (due in part to excellent weather conditions and in part to successful agricultural development efforts) , India will still require significant grain imports. Production, at best, continues to lag behind both population growth and increasing needs.

The deteriorating food situation in India in the first half of the 1960's was not entirely unexpected. In 1959, at the request of the Ministry of Food and Agriculture and the Ministry of Community Development, the Ford Foundation sponsored a study of agricultural development prospects. The study, prepared by a team of leading American specialists and entitled *Report on India's Food Crisis and Steps to Meet It,*

---

dustry, community development, electric power, transport, and communications, and for the increased production of each type of commodity and production material falling within the major headings. Each successive plan has called for greater increases in national income and in production than its predecessor and has reflected somewhat different ideas as to priorities. For example, the Second Five-Year Plan was twice the size of the first and involved a shift of emphasis from agriculture toward large-scale industry. The Third Five-Year Plan also called for a larger investment in industry than in agriculture.

predicted a food crisis by 1966 unless the rate of increase in food production was tripled. The report recommended that food production be given highest priority and suggested a set of policies and programs for more rapid agricultural development. These recommendations are generally as valid today as they were in 1959.

TABLE 3

TOTAL PRODUCTION, IMPORTS, AND AVAILABILITY OF FOOD GRAINS
IN INDIA, 1949–50 THROUGH 1967–68, WITH PER CAPITA COMPARISONS

Crop Year	Production	Importsa	Availability	Per Capita Production	Per Capita Availability
	(in million metric tons)			*(in kilograms)*	
1949–50	60.7	2.2	62.9	168.0	173.8
1950–51	54.9	4.8	59.7	151.1	164.3
1951–52	55.5	3.9	59.4	150.2	160.8
1952–53	61.7	2.0	63.7	164.1	169.4
1953–54	72.2	.8	73.0	188.6	190.7
1954–55	70.6	.7	71.3	181.0	182.8
1955–56	69.2	1.4	70.6	174.0	177.6
1956–57	72.3	3.6	75.9	178.2	187.1
1957–58	66.5	3.2	69.7	160.6	168.3
1958–59	78.7	4.0	82.7	186.0	195.5
1959–60	76.7	5.2	81.9	177.3	189.3
1960–61	82.0	3.6	85.6	185.3	193.4
1961–62	82.7	3.7	86.4	182.5	190.6
1962–63	78.5	4.6	83.1	169.1	179.0
1963–64	80.2	6.4	86.6	168.7	182.2
1964–65	89.0	7.6	96.6	182.8	198.4
1965–66	72.3	10.2	82.5	145.0	165.4
1966–67	76.0	8.9	84.9	148.8	166.3
1967–68	95.0	...	...	181.7	...

a On a calendar-year basis, e.g., imports of 4.8 million metric tons for 1950–51 are for the calendar year 1951.

Although the Ford Foundation report received serious attention within the Indian Government, those who were convinced that agriculture should be given top priority were unable to get this recommendation incorporated into the Third Five-Year Plan, covering the period 1961–62 through 1965–66. The plan did call for a very large increase in resources to develop both agriculture and industry; but, as in earlier years, industry was given the higher priority.

EMPHASIS ON HEAVY INDUSTRY

India's stress on industrial development, even at the expense of agriculture, and its stress on government ownership or control as against private enterprise, is rooted in history. Its more than 500 million people, taken as a whole, are among the most impoverished in the world. Many Indians believe that the basic cause of their impoverishment goes back to Imperial England's policy of draining wealth out of the country and manipulating the economy for British gain. English rulers discouraged the development of competitive industry in India, while increasing agricultural production without proper attention to improvement of the land. They encouraged production of high-priced goods for a limited Indian market. These practices not only prejudiced the Indian Government against foreign rulers and foreign industry, but led to a distrust of private industrial development. That many Indian industrial families have also tended to seek large short-term gains, rather than long steady growth, has not helped to dispel this antagonism toward private ownership.

As a consequence, India has feared a concentration of economic power that would not be strictly accountable to the public interest. Its concern over the development of private economic power led to the adoption of the Industrial Policy Resolution in 1948. As revised in 1956, this resolution, divided industry into three groups. Development of the first group, which included iron, coal, and oil, was to be the "exclusive responsibility of the state"; the second, which included fertilizers, heavy chemicals, and essential drugs, was to "be progressively state-owned," with the government taking the initiative in establishing new undertakings; and the third was to be left, in general, "to the initiative and enterprise of the private sector." Spurred by the food crisis, the Government of India has begun to relax these restrictions. Among other changes, it is now actively stimulating the investment of both domestic and foreign private capital in the fertilizer industry, originally designated for state ownership.

It is not difficult to understand why India and other developing countries would tend to see industrialization as a quicker road to development than increased agricultural production. Agriculture involves millions of small individual producers who must be educated and provided with incentives and materials for production. With new industries, it is possible simply to import the necessary machines and the technological processes. Furthermore, to a considerable extent, the new industries, with their special patterns of organization and techniques, can operate uninhibited by the years of custom and tradition that impede change in agriculture. The possibility of concentrating industries in modern cities and the smaller number of people required to manage and operate them, as compared with the large number of farmers, makes for quicker accomplishment of a more tangible goal. As former President of the World Bank, George D. Woods once said, concerning politicians of developing countries: "[industry] appears as the wave of the future, while [agriculture] suggests stagnation and subjugation associated with the past."

Indian emphasis on the use of scarce resources for heavy industry was additionally reinforced by faith that improved community development almost alone could solve the agricultural problem. Better village organization to teach farmers to make use of simple measures already known to' improve yields, it was believed, could bring about a large increase in production. Some of the reliance on community development as the answer to food production goes back to Mahatma Gandhi's ideal of the self-sufficient village economy, which he saw as the appropriate base for the regeneration of the traditional Indian community—and, significantly, the Community Development Program was launched on Gandhi's birthday in 1952.

The Government of India not only gave secondary priority to agriculture in the targets set for the Third Five-Year Plan, but also failed to achieve what the plan projected. India aimed at increasing food grain production in that period by 20 million metric tons—from 82 million metric tons in 1960–61 to 102 million metric tons in 1965–66. Because of the drought, as noted above, actual production in the last year of the plan was about 72 million metric tons. But even if India had experienced average weather conditions, production that year would probably have been not more than 90 million metric tons.

SHORTAGE OF AGRICULTURAL SUPPLIES

Inadequate production was due in large part to inability to meet targets for increases in vital supplies. Increases in fertilizer fell far short of those planned. Actual increases during the Third Five-Year Plan were 60 per cent of that planned for nitrogenous fertilizers, about 40 per cent for phosphate fertilizers, and only 50 per cent for potash fertilizer. Similarly, only about 70 per cent of the goals for improved seed and plant protection measures were realized. And the cost of all these materials, essential to a sharp increase in production, remained very high in relation to the selling price of the products.

LOW PRICES FOR PRODUCTS

In addition to the lack of agricultural production materials, Indian farmers were faced with low prices for their products, particularly food products. The Government of India had

long followed a price policy designed to keep food prices low
to consumers. This policy had also kept farm prices down. As
a result, farmers had no financial incentive to invest in fertilizer, improved seed, irrigation, and the other requisites for
rapidly expanding food output. This unfavorable price relationship persisted for several years. Unhappily, its continu-
ance was made possible in large measure by grain received
from the United States under P.L. 480.

It is readily apparent that not only were agricultural development targets too modest, but India also had an inadequate
performance record. This inadequacy was allowed to persist
in spite of the fact that the authors of *Report on India's Food
Crisis and Steps to Meet It* (a) predicted that a food crisis
would develop if agricultural development was approached
on a "business as usual" basis; (b) identified the key com-
ponents of a successful agricultural development program,
including incentive prices, an abundant supply of physical
production materials, research and education, adequate credit,
and better markets; and (c) clearly pointed out that top priority would have to be given to agricultural development and
that it was within India's capabilities to achieve satisfactory
rates of growth in food production.

When I visited India in 1964, I was distressed by the lack
of progress made in agriculture. It was clear that disaster
could be averted only if a new, bold, and vigorous approach
were taken by the Government of India, and by the United
States and other countries providing economic assistance.

All along, India had planned its agricultural development,
but little progress had been made. The agricultural assistance
program of the United States had been and still was spotty
and weak. We had nothing approximating a total strategy for
agricultural development in India; there was no official U.S.
blueprint for action. Instead, there was a tendency to take
India's plans at face value, even though its performance rec-

ord was weak. The United States had not held India to minimum agricultural performance commitments that were part of the long-term P.L. 480 agreements. In general, the United States had not insisted on measurable progress as a *quid pro quo* for food and technical assistance. Rather, we had provided India with increasing food assistance and had insisted on very little progress in return.

In all, at that time, over $2.5 billion worth of American farm products had been shipped to India since the P.L. 480 program had begun. (Since then, the amount has risen to $3.8 billion, with a sharp increase in response to the drought-year needs in 1966 and 1967.) During those years, we had had hundreds of U.S. technicians working in India, and nearly 2,000 Indians had come to the United States for advanced training in agriculture.

The need to improve price incentives to farmers was one of the major items that I discussed with Indian officials during my 1964 visit. Later that year, India requested assistance from the U.S. AID mission to help formulate and implement a price-support program for food grains. A team of experts from the Department of Agriculture went to India in the summer of 1964, and, early the next year, the Food Corporation of India was established. Its principal function is to operate a price-support mechanism that will ensure incentive-level prices to food grain producers. The Indian Government has established minimum prices to be reviewed annually. The United States continues to supply technical assistance for the Food Corporation to help it become an effective institution for implementing a national food price policy in India.

Food shortages in the past few years have resulted in sharp increases in market prices that are now well above support levels. Today, farmers have ample price incentives. As the Food Corporation increases its capabilities it can guarantee that prices will not fall to unfavorably low levels when rapid increases in food output are achieved.

THE CRITICAL NEEDS TODAY

On my most recent trip to India, in July, 1966, I witnessed the response of Indian farmers to improved prices. The demand for fertilizers and improved seed had increased dramatically; farmers were clamoring for them. A short span of time had shattered the myth that farmers were bound by centuries of tradition. It had become readily apparent to almost everyone that the peasant cultivators of India, when properly motivated and given something to work with, were, indeed, dynamic people. Farmers in India, like those in other countries, are willing to work and to invest to increase production when it is profitable. I have met farmers all over the world who could not read and write, but I have never met a farmer who could not count.

Price incentives, however, are just a stimulus. Farmers must have modern tools to increase their food production. In India, there continues to be a crying need for more fertilizer, improved seeds, pesticides, better irrigation methods and soil management practices, and credit at reasonable interest rates and on terms better suited to investments in agricultural production.

Where were all these materials and methods to come from in adequate amounts and in time to avert a serious food crisis? Clearly, a well-structured emergency program was needed for Indian agricultural development. When I returned to the United States, I discussed this problem with Administrator David Bell of AID and with President Johnson. I outlined what I thought India would have to do, and what the United States could do, to help avert a serious food crisis. I stressed that the United States should insist on numerous self-help measures by India. These measures were later explicitly embodied in the Food for Freedom legislation.

During the droughts of 1965–67, there was a growing awareness in India that a greater effort was needed in agriculture. It had become clear that India could not afford in the future to rely on ever-increasing amounts of food aid; there was already a limit to how much food was available and how much could be moved through India's ports. India, under the leadership of the then Minister of Food and Agriculture C. Subramanian, realized that it could not achieve its long-run economic development goals as long as the country was becoming more and more dependent on outside food aid.

Thus, in late 1965, representatives from the Government of India, the United States, and the World Bank, which has been much interested in agricultural development, began to work out a new strategy for Indian agricultural development. This strategy included planning, but it strongly stressed quick performance—for time was short.

The first need was for the Government of India to recognize that agriculture was the backbone of its economy and to act accordingly. The Indian Government proceeded by announcing that, except for national defense, agriculture would be given the highest priority in development policies and programs. Prime Minister Indira Gandhi, in a broadcast on April 25, 1966, expressed her government's determination to solve the food problem:

The current drought has a lesson for us. It is absolutely imperative that agricultural productivity is improved to a point where, taking the good years with the bad, we have a reasonable margin of safety. We simply cannot afford another gamble in rains. . . . The present food situation shows how vitally important it is for us to attain an output of 120 to 125 million tons of food grain by 1971. If we fail in this then . . . the whole economy will be thrown out of gear with incalculable human, social, economic, and political consequences.

In another speech, Mrs. Gandhi stressed that agriculture is the crucial problem in the economy:

The long term lesson we have drawn from this famine is that it is necessary in agriculture to produce enough not only to be self-sufficient, but a little more. That is the basic objective of the bold new agricultural strategy that has been evolved in India in the last year. This strategy has been based on an intensive review, which has lasted for several months preceding the present crisis. Basically, what we are attempting is to break the vicious circle of poor incentives, inadequate inputs, and low production in Indian agriculture and to modernize agriculture within a short space of time.

Expenditures planned for agricultural development during the years 1966–71 are nearly double those of the Third Five-Year Plan for the years 1960–65. And there is evidence that India intends to carry out its strengthened agricultural programs. Expenditures on agriculture have increased substantially. At a 1966 budget meeting of the chief ministers of the Indian states, various budget items were trimmed back, but the expanded agricultural portion of the budget remained untouched. It was unanimously agreed that agriculture must be spared any cut. At last, agriculture was receiving the top-level attention that had been needed for so long.

By this time, it was clear, too, that immediate steps had to be taken to increase the availability of a wide variety of agricultural production goods. During the period of the Third Five-Year Plan, there had been only a token increase in these materials. This meant not only making up for shortages that were carried over from the Third Five-Year Plan, but also ensuring that the supply of agricultural production goods would expand at a rate rapid enough to meet the needs projected. Following discussions among representatives from India, the United States, and the World Bank, the Government of India adopted a general policy of making sufficient foreign exchange available to import the quantity of agricultural production materials required to fill the gap between domestic production and expected needs. This policy represented a sharp departure from previous practices; formerly, foreign exchange had been reserved mainly for the importation of industrial items not directly related to agricultural needs.

FERTILIZER

One of the most critical needs was (and still is) for fertilizer. In 1966, the Government of India announced a set of realistic targets, based on a hard appraisal of future fertilizer needs, for total fertilizer availability, domestic production, and import requirements (see Table 4). This plan will require very substantial amounts of foreign exchange over the next five years to finance high levels of imports, because domestic production will fall far short of total requirements.

TABLE 4

PLANNED AVAILABILITY OF FERTILIZER, BY SOURCE, IN INDIA,
1966–67 THROUGH 1970–71
(in million metric nutrient tons)

Crop Year	Nitrogen (N)			Phosphate (P$_2$O$_5$)			Potassium (K$_2$O)
	Require-ments	Domestic Produc-tion	Import Require-ments	Require-ments	Domestic Produc-tion	Import Require-ments	Import Require-ments
1966–67	1.000	0.400	0.600	0.370	0.190	0.180	0.200
1967–68	1.385	0.535	0.850	0.500	0.275	0.225	0.300
1968–69	1.700	0.763	0.937	0.650	0.365	0.285	0.450
1969–70	2.000	1.104	0.896	0.800	0.410	0,390	0.550
1970–71	2.400	1.700	0.700	1.000	0.520	0.480	0.700

The lag in domestic production capacity reflects the inadequate policies of the Government of India in this sphere. Prior to 1966, India had depended heavily on public production and distribution of fertilizer. This policy had several very serious shortcomings—the main one being that the government did not have, and does not now have, the managerial capacity to construct and operate fertilizer plants efficiently.

It has taken an average of seven years to bring a public ferti-lizer plant into production. Moreover, existing plants were operating at not much more than 60 per cent of capacity.

In this situation, India had only one alternative. It had to attract foreign private capital to do the job that the government had proved unable to do. Early in 1966 came the announcement of a new policy, designed to expand fertilizer production rapidly through foreign private investment. It made such investment more attractive by allowing foreigners to hold majority ownership of new plants and by removing or reducing many bureaucratic stumbling blocks to private investment. Under the announced policy, private firms that agreed before March 1, 1967, to build fertilizer plants in India would be allowed to price and distribute the fertilizer, rather than having to depend upon government pricing and distribution, as in the past. The Government of India also agreed to buy, at negotiated prices, a percentage of each plant's production. The investment climate was improved by the assurance to owners of new plants that there would not be temporary and geographically limited surpluses of fertilizer.

This policy led to completion of some lagging investment negotiations and attracted several new fertilizer investments to India. American firms, as well as those of several other countries, continue to have a keen interest in investing in fertilizer production in India. No less important, Indian firms are becoming more involved in fertilizer production. Efforts to improve operations and output from existing fertilizer plants have also improved the investment climate for new private ventures by Indian nationals. Foreign exchange has been made available to import raw materials and spare parts. The production of existing plants has increased from around 60 per cent to over 80 per cent of capacity. Also, the liberalization of imports has reduced the estimated time required to bring a plant into production to an average of four years.

IMPROVED SEEDS

Along with fertilizer, India needs improved varieties of seeds. Improved native varieties—particularly wheat and rice —tolerate only limited amounts of fertilizer. High levels of fertilization needed to give large increases in yields have caused excessive plant growth and the tendency to fall over, known as lodging. In the case of wheat, these difficulties have been removed by introducing new varieties from Mexico, where the plants have been bred in a program run by the Rockefeller Foundation and the Mexican Government. Similarly, improved varieties of rice imported from Taiwan and the Philippines are giving good results under Indian growing conditions. Diseases that will reduce the productivity of the new imported seeds will undoubtedly develop. The new varieties developed in other countries may not be resistant to plant diseases present in India. Additional breeding work will almost certainly be necessary to give the new varieties a built-in resistance to diseases. But the progress is heartening.

On my 1966 visit, I was impressed with the realistic and dynamic attitude of Indian researchers toward possible trouble with the new varieties of wheat and rice. They were well aware of the problems and were gearing their research program to meet them. But, at the same time, recognizing the urgent need for increased food production, they were actively pushing the multiplication and distribution of the imported varieties, knowing that such action is risky but necessary. Through 1967 the new varieties had held up well.

It is particularly encouraging to note the progress being made in multiplying and distributing the new seeds. There is a strong demand for them, and they are selling at high prices, thus making the seed business newly profitable. Private enterprise is responding rapidly, working cooperatively with government researchers and government seed production and distribution agencies.

The private involvement ranges from large seed farms—one operated by an American firm and another by a large Indian firm—to individual villages that are producing, processing, and distributing seed. Prospects are good for the rapid expansion of private enterprise in the seed business. Again, this reflects a change in government policy. Previously, the heavy emphasis was governmental, but the administrative machinery was not equal to the task. The mobilization of private enterprise should ensure a successful, improved seed program, and, if the expansion in production of improved seed varieties continues at its present rate, India should be able to meet its immediate needs within a few years.

Intensive Development

Despite the progress being made, India will have a shortage of key agricultural production goods for some time to come. To get the greatest food output from available resources, it is necessary to concentrate them, to the extent practicable, in the most productive areas. As long as demand is strong, market forces will pull resources into these areas. But market forces are not the only allocating device; government administration still plays an important role, particularly with respect to education and extension programs to teach farmers how to use new production materials most effectively. The United States has pressed the Government of India to develop such programs.

This concept is by no means new. The 1959 Ford Foundation report on India's food crisis gave special attention to the improvement of extension work through community development, stating that "India's village families—men, women and children—hold the key to increased food production." The specialists recommended that certain crops and areas—to be chosen on the basis of their potentialities for increasing production—receive intensive agricultural development efforts. This recommendation was incorporated in the Third Five-Year Plan.

The Ford Foundation provided financial assistance for the organization of an initial group of seven pilot districts, selected on the basis of production potential within certain geographic areas. During 1962–63, the seven districts were expanded to fifteen. The aim of the "Intensive Agricultural Districts Program," as it was called, was to acquaint producers with the use of a "package" of production materials, including fertilizer, improved seed, pesticides, and irrigation, and to demonstrate the benefit to be derived from their interaction. Although the goal of expanding agricultural production by 12 per cent annually was not realized, or even closely approached, substantial progress was made in many of the districts.

The Intensive Agricultural Districts Program was expanded during 1964–65 and renamed the "Intensive Agricultural Areas Program." Its objective was to cover approximately 114 areas, selected on the basis of potential for development. It is now being followed by the "High-Yielding Varieties Program," which will cover some 32 million acres by 1971. Under this program, farmers are to get adequate supplies of new seed varieties, fertilizers, pesticides, new farm implements, and credit.

USE OF IRRIGATION

One of India's greatest long-term agricultural needs is the development of its water resources. India has one of the largest potential water supplies of any country in the world, but its use has been tied to tradition. With adequate irrigation, two or even three crops a year can be produced on most of India's farmland. With more fertilizers, improved seed, and pesticides, the lack of adequate intensive irrigation can quickly become the major obstacle to improving agricultural output.

The Indian subcontinent has a long history of irrigation. Hindu kings developed irrigation systems that were strikingly large and bold for their time. Before British rule, Muslim rulers diverted the waters of some northern rivers into canals. The British Government of India developed a wide network of irrigation canals, using the waters of the Ganges River. By 1947, when it became independent, India had 50 million acres of land under irrigation—more than any other nation in the world.

Although India has continued to develop irrigation projects, the country's turbaned farmers still think of irrigation as a measure for drought protection, rather than for regular use to increase the output from their fields. For years, farmers were reluctant to take water from the canals because of the fees that they had to pay. After the fees were removed, they were still hesitant to level their fields and build the necessary small connecting canals. In his ironic way, Prime Minister Nehru got to the heart of the problem—education. He suggested major dam projects be treated as pilgrimage centers for modern India, and that pictures of the new dams, garlanded with flowers, be hung alongside the pictures of the gods in farm homes.

Somewhat belatedly, the Government of India has recognized that the limited concept of irrigation as drought relief is not sufficient to inspire farmers to action. Now the need to change the old concept to one of irrigation to produce bigger crops has led to high priority being given to the installation of small tube wells and the restoration of old facilities wherever work can be completed within a short time. There is evidence of high pay-off from tube wells, which individual farmers can control and use for double, or even triple, cropping. With price supports and other measures to ensure price stability, and with technicians to help with the design of proper irrigation structures for intensive agriculture, irrigation can be a major factor in increasing production. But a crash program of more persuasion and more construction is needed now.

At the end of 1967, the U.S. Department of Agriculture had a team of soil and water experts in India, working with their colleagues on soil and water management problems. They have made policy and program recommendations. India will have to follow through quickly if lack of water is not to be a major deterrent to agricultural development. As pointed out in Chapter 4, maximum results are obtained from fertilizer and improved seed only when these are combined with adequate quantities of water. Thus, the supply of irrigation water will have to expand at least as fast as supplies of fertilizer and improved seed.

BETTER CREDIT

Finally, there has been great concern in many quarters over the inadequacy of the present agricultural credit system in India. This is another area in which the U.S. Government has pressed the Government of India for more rapid action. The future agricultural credit needs of India, and how these needs can best be met, are being studied and tested by Indian officials.

Up to now, agricultural credit has not been a serious constraint on increasing food production. But, as the supply of production resources increases and as favorable incentives stimulate farmers to make a variety of longer-term investments (such as tube wells), the demand for credit will increase very sharply. Also, the type of credit needed will change. Most agricultural credit available in India today is short-term. It works for financing current operating expenses, but is not satisfactory for longer-term investments that can reasonably be paid off only in five to seven years.

The traditional sources of credit for Indian farmers are family savings, local moneylenders, and cooperative credit societies. With moneylenders, interest rates are very high and credit is short-term in nature. In the cooperative credit societies, interest rates are reasonable, but the cooperatives have had a poor record of getting adequate amounts of credit to farmers when it is needed. It is unlikely that the cooperatives can improve their efficiency and diversify their credit programs sufficiently to meet India's rapidly growing agricultural credit needs.

India needs a fresh new approach to agricultural credit. New policies and new institutions will have to be evolved, and they should be national in scope. More thought should be given to the establishment of a national credit institution capable of supplying both short- and long-term credit. Such an institution would complement rather than substitute for existing credit institutions. In addition, steps should be taken to improve the performance of cooperative credit societies, and the private banking system should be strongly encouraged to extend credit to farmers. Because improvement in agricultural credit in India requires institution building, which takes time, and because the demands for such credit are increasing very rapidly, the government should proceed posthaste.

SOME CONCLUSIONS

As an observer of Indian agricultural development, I am impressed by the progress made in both India and the United States in shaping a realistic approach to India's agricultural problems. The self-help measures initiated by the Government of India in the last two years are a good start. Through these and related measures, India hopes to become self-sufficient in food production by 1971. Agriculture, according to Mrs. Gandhi, has "been placed on top of the list of all developmental schemes, whether for allocation of internal or external resources." A key decision in carrying out this policy is that innovations by farmers are to be made profitable through adequate price incentives. Thus, the increased use of fertilizer, irrigation, improved seeds, pesticides, and other materials for production should more than pay for themselves. The government is determined to make production materials and adequate credit available. India can be proud of its progress to date. Indian planners now realize that all phases of national development depend upon a breakthrough in agriculture. (They also realize that Indian farmers, like farmers in America, will produce for profit—and not as a result of exhortation.)

I would add one word of warning. Progress comes rapidly when the most productive farmers are reached. Experience shows, however, that it may then slow down; it will resume only through determined leadership effort.

During the last few years, while India's leaders were examining their policies and deciding that agriculture was the basic key to development, the United States has given its foreign assistance program a searching review. One inescapable conclusion has been that we have tended to scatter our assistance on large numbers of piecemeal projects. Little hard-headed attention has been given to broad issues and plans for economic development in India. For example, during the 1950's we provided assistance for as many as eighty agricultural education and research institutions. Because the training in these institutions was largely theoretical, our assistance made only minor contributions to the immediate problems of agricultural development. Since 1963, we have been concentrating our assistance on the building up of seven independent agricultural universities, which will have state-wide programs of agricultural research, teaching, and extension. The universities are located in seven states, which include about 40 per cent of India's arable land, 60 per cent of its cropped and irrigated land, and a little over 50 per cent of the country's population.

Most important, today we are more realistic about what it is going to take to make India self-sufficient in food production. We realize that there must be a tremendous effort by India herself. We also realize that India is going to need large amounts of outside resources, both from private and government sources, to achieve a satisfactory rate of agricultural development. Above all, we realize that the outside assistance can be effective only if India gives top priority to planning and action to agricultural development. We have made it crystal clear that our food and technical assistance will be shared only if India makes her own determined effort. Many things remain to be done quickly and effectively. Policies and programs that are adequate to meet today's goals may fall woefully short of meeting tomorrow's objectives. Although some of the policy changes that have been instituted by the Government of India represent sharp departures from the past, they may not yet be bold enough to meet future needs for such things as fertilizer, water, pesticides, price incentives, credit, processing, and marketing. And Indian Government leaders have yet to prove that planning can be translated into effective, active programs on a sustained basis.

India became a pilot project—an extremely large one—in self-help efforts before the principle of self-help was incorporated in our legislation. The experience to date indicates that, with sufficient will and determination and with effective support from other nations, a developing country such as India can get its agriculture moving. Since India's new self-help program is consistent with the goals of our Food for Freedom program, I am confident that the United States will continue to help India in her efforts to achieve agricultural self-sufficiency.

❧

Farming and Food for the Future

❧

The balance between man and food is more precarious today than ever before. Simply to maintain this balance poses a great challenge. Tipping the scale toward a more favorable balance involves changes in traditional behavior by billions of people.

THE REQUIREMENTS

One requirement is that world population must be stabilized within the next thirty-five years. This reversal of present trends calls for changes in age-old attitudes about families. It calls for the universal availability of the means to limit the number of births and for new incentives to hold down family size. In the decade of the 1960's, we have taken the first faltering steps in this direction. The barriers are coming down. The movement is gaining momentum. There is hope.

The other requirement is that food production must be increased, especially in those countries that now have too little food for too many people. Generally, in these countries, the tiller of the soil is at the bottom of the social and economic ladder with little incentive to produce more than enough to feed his family. His situation must be changed.

Let me recapitulate briefly. Exploding population makes it vital that every acre of land on this earth be used to the best advantage. Yet in many parts of the world rivers run red, brown, or yellow with eroded soil. Hillsides are denuded and newly built water storage reservoirs are silting up. Despite the world-wide shortage of fresh water, we continue to pollute streams and lakes.

Research has shown us how we can solve these problems. Hillsides bare for centuries can be reforested. Soil erosion can be stopped. Abused soil can be returned to productivity. We have learned how to find water, stretch it, conserve it, and reuse it. We are on the verge of being able to desalinate it so efficiently that man's fresh water needs can be supplied from the seas.

We have learned to breed plants so precisely that they can be tailored to specialized climatic and soil conditions and can resist diseases, satisfy food preferences, and meet the requirements of commercial marketing. We also know how to increase yields as much as fourfold, through optimum use of improved varieties, water, fertilizer, and pesticides. We have learned much about the social and economic factors that promote or inhibit changes in men's actions.

In the summer of 1963, I traveled to the Soviet Union, Poland, Rumania, and Yugoslavia to study and discuss their agriculture. In all of these nations, production was far behind that in the United States. Understandably, agricultural scientists in those nations are eager to learn more about our technology, even though they shy away from our efficient, privately owned family farm system. I urged then, and still urge, that, in the interests of peace, we exchange agricultural ideas, experts, and farmers. Actually, some of the products of our technology, such as hybrid corn, are being widely adopted in the Communist countries. This sharing of knowledge and achievements is good for everyone. We need such bridges.

THE PROBLEMS REMAINING

But so far our knowledge has been applied in comparatively few areas. Why? Food is survival. Methods of food production and use are the result of millenniums of practical experience. They are deeply rooted in tradition and religion. Food is produced by great numbers of individual farmers under an infinite variety of physical and economic conditions. To increase food production significantly, proven new combinations of practices suited to the individual farm must be available, and be convincingly demonstrated. The struggling farmer must believe that he will be better off if he adopts the new practices. But he doesn't convince easily. The stranger, be he from a faraway country or from an agricultural school in the nearest city, is not always trusted. Improved practices sometimes fail to produce the expected results, due to the capriciousness of weather. A bountiful harvest may result in a temporary surplus in the market place and in low prices to the producers. Compound all these problems by adding insecure land tenure, lack of credit, poor transportation, inadequate processing and storage, widespread illiteracy, and lack of trained agricultural leaders. The wonder is not that change is slow—but that change is possible at all.

Change has to come. Traditional argiculture must be modernized. The world must double, triple, in some places quadruple, agricultural production in the years ahead. I believe the job can be done. My reasons for this belief stem from personal experience and observations since I became Secretary of Agriculture in 1961.

Consider some of the changes under way in the 1960's.

Only in this decade have we really begun to face up to the problem of the world's insufficient food supply.

A CHANGING APPROACH

During the 1950's, we hoped to make up shortages in particular areas simply by shipping food abroad. Now we realize that we must do all we can to encourage people abroad to produce more food. And, on that score, we have made some progress. Many thousands of American agricultural technicians, teachers, and scientists have worked in developing countries, and they have done much good. In some countries, a basic structure of agricultural research and educational institutions has been laid, which will make increasingly significant contributions to agricultural development.

But it is in the administration of agricultural assistance that we have completely changed our attitude toward promoting food production abroad. When I became Secretary of Agriculture, neither the U.S. Government nor the FAO had detailed information about world food needs, present or future. Since then, the researchers in the Department of Agriculture have brought together a series of increasingly precise world food budgets showing current needs and projected future needs. Now we can focus on the problem much more sharply.

As data from these studies has revealed the gravity of the race between food and people, agricultural development has assumed the number one priority in U.S. aid programs. Its fundamental importance is clearly understood by American representatives in foreign countries and by planners and administrators in those countries. Agricultural programs are now the first to be considered and analyzed as country programs are developed. Farmers in developing countries seem to have a new awareness of their agricultural practices and a desire to improve them. The change is evidenced by the demand for fertilizers and pesticides, which is now outrunning available supplies.

Other industrialized countries are orienting their foreign-aid programs toward agricultural development. Country after country has acknowledged that each should share in helping to feed the world by contributing food, funds, or agricultural production supplies. Just last year, the principal commercial exporters and importers of food grains agreed to provide a total of 4.5 million metric tons of grain or its cash equivalent per year to the needy nations of the world. This agreement, the Food Aid Convention of the International Grains Arrangement of 1967, also provides for the establishment of a Food Aid Committee to supervise the implementation of the convention.

Public Law 480, which originated as a device to dispose of surplus agricultural commodities, today serves as a program to buy time, so that people in the developing countries can learn to produce enough food to feed themselves. Under its amendments, we are requiring countries that receive food aid to exert themselves to develop their own food production. We don't want American food to be used as a crutch. This position may sound harsh, but it is necessary. Formerly, only commodities in surplus supply could be used in food aid. Today, we have authority to buy the foods we need for food-aid programs—limited only by the requirement that such purchases do not create domestic food shortages and that commercial export demands are met. We have authority to process, fortify, and combine various raw food commodities to provide optimum nutrition in food-aid programs. Thus, the new P.L. 480 program is a positive approach to meeting world food needs.

In addition we have changed the orientation of our agricultural export and agricultural adjustment programs for American farmers. The Food and Agriculture Act of 1965 gives us a flexible domestic farm program so that we can produce the commodities we need to meet food requirements at home and abroad. Under this program, we can encourage American farmers to adjust production between various crops and to produce enough oilseeds, as well as enough wheat and corn. We call this getting the "right mix." It is a way to make effective use of our tremendous agricultural potential.

These two programs, the modernized P.L. 480 and the Food and Agriculture Act of 1965, supplement each other. Combined, they make it possible for the United States to develop for each crop year a "national food budget," under which, in most years, we can produce enough of what is needed, but not so much that farm prices are depressed. When sharp variations in production are triggered by uncontrollable weather or environmental factors, adjustments can be made in acreage and in the volume of P.L. 480 sales, within limits that are not unduly disruptive, so that supply and demand are brought back into workable balance. Such a system will help American farmers reach the parity of income that they are entitled to, and at the same time permit the necessary planning for an effective food-assistance program.

It will not be simple or easy to use these new tools and to develop and operate a national food budget effectively. Some difficulties came into sharp focus in 1966 and in 1967. In the early fall of 1966, it was my responsibility as Secretary of Agriculture to set acreage allotments for wheat, feed grains, soybeans, and rice for the coming year. At that time, the world food supply was very tight. The grain surplus in the United States had been eliminated. We had necessary reserves, although they were a bit on the short side. Crop prospects around the world were predicted as moderate to limited. World demand was booming. With all this, the worst drought in a century hit India. It looked as if we needed to increase production to meet anticipated shortages.

After broad consultation and careful review of all the facts,

I made the decision to increase sharply the acreage of grain. This decision was thoughtfully made, taking into consideration estimated world needs and carry-over. Our predictions, however, proved substantially wrong. The weather was exceptionally good everywhere. Instead of a short crop, 1967 proved to be one of the best years in history. Canada, Western Europe, Australia, Argentina, South Africa, and Thailand harvested excellent crops. In one year's time, the world supply situation turned full circle. The result was temporary oversupply, with severe downward pressure on farm prices—particularly in the United States, where wheat, corn, and soybeans dropped 25–50 cents a bushel. American farmers were understandably unhappy. Corrective action was taken, however. Just as we acted to increase acreage in 1966, at a time of threatened shortage, so, in developing the national food budget for 1967–68, a time of surplus, we acted to curtail grain production. The result will be a smaller crop in the United States in 1968 and, presumably, stronger farm prices. At the same time, adequate supplies will be maintained. Again, unusual weather or environmental conditions could sharply alter this situation either way.

We have to operate subject to the extremes of shortage and surplus, seeking to hold a workable balance between supply and demand that will ensure a fair price to producers and a constant supply to meet our needs and to expedite development around the world. With this constraint, it is unfortunate that we have been facing in the years 1966–68 an unusual variation in the weather pattern, which has twice, so far, sharply changed the volume of production. Such fluctuation is disconcerting to producers in the United States and users under P.L. 480 around the world. It would have been much simpler if the national food budget could have proved itself during a more normal period. I have complete confidence, however, that we now have the tools that, if skillfully used, will make it possible to balance supply and demand. Our new capacity to cushion the impact of the production swings of the last few years will build confidence in the food budget system as it becomes better understood.

WHERE TWENTY YEARS HAVE LED US

Many sincere and honest people feel that twenty years of foreign aid should have cured the world's ills, if they could be cured by aid. It is true that in twenty years we have made only a small dent in over-all technical assistance and in food assistance. Few people realize, however, how much has been accomplished, particularly in establishing a framework for action. Twenty years ago there had never been a world-wide census. Today we are preparing for the second world census. Twenty years ago, there was no World Bank, no regional bank, no International Monetary Fund. There was no world-wide technical-assistance program like that the United Nations now operates, and no organized bilateral technical-assistance program. In short, the concept and the whole framework for the international transfer of resources and technology have been built in the last twenty years.

Twenty years ago, access to higher education was the privilege of the wealthy, and free public elementary education was largely confined to Europe and North America. Today, advanced national education systems have been built, curriculums devised, and teachers trained, and hundreds of millions of children attend schools in villages and hamlets around the world. We can look forward to greatly increased literacy, which, in turn, will make technological change in agriculture more readily attainable.

Our investments in foreign aid have paid off and are continuing to pay off. Aid in the form of loans is being repaid and loaned again. Some local-currency funds generated under P.L. 480 are financing second-generation economic-development loans. The countries that received Marshall Plan aid are now aid donors.

I believe that the achievements of the past twenty years have been spectacular, but they have been inadequate in the face of total need. We have expected to accomplish too much in too short a period with too little effort. At a time when they should have been increasing, our expenditures on foreign aid have been declining, both in dollars and in terms of our growing capacity. Our total aid effort has had relatively low priority, even though we have been giving increasing emphasis to food aid. We have been more concerned about other needs. Some years ago, we subscribed to the principle that each developed country should contribute at least 1 per cent of its national income annually to help the poor nations. The U.S. contribution has declined to seven-tenths of 1 per cent. One of the last actions of Congress in 1967 was to reduce foreign aid to its lowest level in twenty years.

We have made other mistakes. The keys to sound development—family planning, agriculture, and education—were neglected until recently. We underestimated the obstacles and overestimated the transferability of technology. We promised more than we could deliver, sometimes starting a chain reaction of disillusionment and distrust, which has increased the difficulty of development.

The road ahead is long and hard. The sands of time are running fast. We have no more than fifteen to twenty years to bring man and his food supply into balance. The Panel on the World Food Supply of the President's Science Advisory Committee spent more than a year in intensive study before releasing its report in May, 1967. That report recommends, without a single dissenting voice, that the United States provide strong initiative and leadership in the world-wide war on hunger. We can meet the challenge of a hungry world, but we need courage and long-term commitment. Now, the time has come to set concrete goals to demonstrate our willingness to lead. I propose a basic, long-term commitment of our resources to the war on hunger. To begin with, I strongly urge Congress to give immediate attention to renewing P.L. 480 and the Food and Agriculture Act of 1965.

NEW TARGETS IN NUTRITION

In November, 1967, in an address to members of the FAO meeting in Rome, I proposed the following short-term targets in the vital area of nutrition:

(1) that all emergency shipments of wheat and corn flour be fortified with vitamins, minerals, and proteins by 1969;
(2) that all imports of wheat and all wheat products in large urban milling centers in developing countries be fortified by 1970;
(3) that 1 billion more cups of protein beverage per day be produced by 1970; and
(4) that efforts be redoubled to produce and gain consumer acceptance for fortified rice.

We should now set longer-range nutrition targets. Food-aid programs—our own and those of multilateral agencies such as the World Food Program—should be redirected specifically and increasingly toward eliminating malnutrition in children. The goal should be nutritionally adequate diets for infants and preschool children throughout the world, plus school lunch programs that would ensure continued adequate nutrition. Food aid with this emphasis would have several advantages. The foods thus provided would be truly additional—that is, they would not replace any usual market demands—and for that reason they could be provided in substantial volume without affecting either international trade or incentives to local producers. They would constitute an essential investment in the most valuable resource of all developing countries—their people.

A Ten-Year Commitment to Technical Assistance

Next, I propose that the United States establish a goal to commit each year, for ten years, 1.5 per cent of its national income to development, with emphasis on technical assistance in food production. Our immediate goal should be to achieve a total flow of resources, governmental and private, of 1 per cent of our national income. This would mean an immediate increase of $2 billion yearly. (In 1966, 1 per cent would have been $6.6 billion, as compared with the $4.6 billion actually transferred. Of the latter, $3.6 billion came from government and $1 billion from private investment and lending.)

As soon as this immediate goal is achieved, and when we, in cooperation with the developing nations, have made sound plans to encourage vastly more self-help, the level should be raised to 1.5 per cent of our national income. Of that total amount, 1 per cent should come from government and the other 0.5 per cent from private investments.

"Agricorp": A Proposal for Private Investors

Private enterprise is becoming increasingly aware of the importance of investing in developing countries. One promising effort lies in the FAO/Industry Cooperative Program, whose activities are financed by several score of major multinational agribusiness companies. It seeks to ring together the managerial, technical, and financial elements for new investments, as well as to cooperate with governments in eliminating obstacles to investment. Despite this and other efforts, private investment naturally tends to flow into the most promising areas, and too often those areas are not the ones where the needs are most urgent. The level of investment and involvement of the private sector of our economy in those most needed areas has therefore lagged. They must be stepped up.

To this end, I propose that we explore suggestions for establishing a private-public corporation, perhaps patterned after Comsat, to deal with agricultural problems. Such a private-public corporation would be financed primarily by the sale of stock to the public, with provision for investment by both the federal government and businesses, including cooperatives, particularly involved in overseas agricultural development. The directors of what we might call "Agricorp" would represent the investing public, the federal government, and concerned private enterprise. Specific objectives for the corporation would have to be studied carefully. I see this corporation as bringing American business knowledge, skills, and financing to such problems as the unified development of a small nation, the establishment of international marketing facilities, the bringing of firms from two or more nations together when that move would be advantageous to everyone concerned, the carrying out of large-scale modernization schemes, and other projects for which large-scale, fully supported effort is essential. Establishment of such a corporation would, of course, require action by Congress.

TRAINED VOLUNTEERS: A PROPOSAL FOR MOBILIZING MANPOWER

Money can be soundly spent, actions firmly taken, and laws carried out only by people—people with dedication and training. Much of our progress in agricultural development so far is due to the 40,000 experienced professionals of the Department of Agriculture and to the staffs of our agricultural colleges and universities. Now we must expand that development with all due speed and skill. We must have the right people working all over the world to make certain that resources, always limited, are used with maximum effectiveness. They must help with the governmental tasks of setting national and regional priorities. In some countries, applied research will be first; in others, marketing. In still others, rural electrification, transportation, fertilizers and chemicals, credit, or combinations of these may command priority. What has come to be known as the "systems" approach to development should be wisely and methodically applied in making decisions as plans are developed and periodically revised, country by country. Certainly, the package approach to agricultural production should be more widely used. The pattern of resource use in our agricultural aid programs is, to my mind, vastly improved over that of ten years ago, when we relied heavily on food aid. But it is still far from perfect—and we do not have enough trained people available to work at it.

Progress is being made to mobilize the skilled manpower essential for this great effort. Participating Agency Service Agreements (PASA), whereby AID contracts with the Department of Agriculture to staff and assume responsibility for agricultural programs in developing countries, are increasing. Professional agriculturists in the Department of Agriculture and perhaps in the land-grant college system should prepare for extended tours in developing countries as a part of their professional careers. But we must attract more young people.

To provide enough agriculturally trained men and women, I propose that the government finance training for qualified volunteers who agree to serve overseas in agricultural development for a period of not less than two years. Those state agricultural colleges that have, or are willing to develop, special research and teaching competences to meet development needs should be selected for participation in this program. Trained young people, who bring enthusiasm, energy, and the simple willingness to dirty their hands in the world's fields and farm sheds, can make a decisive contribution to increasing food production.

All of my proposals—for improved nutrition, commitment of technical assistance, increased private investment where it is most needed, and the mobilization of agricultural professionals and trained volunteers—are set forth because I believe that, in the last half of the twentieth century, we have the opportunity to remove from the face of the earth the threat of famine that Malthus predicted nearly two centuries ago.

We have the opportunity and the responsibility to make the next epoch one that will be known as the Age of the World Without Hunger.

Bibliography

Books

ALLEN, WILLIAM. *The African Husbandman.* New York: Barnes & Noble, 1965.

ANDERSON, C. ARNOLD, and BOWMAN, MARY JEAN (eds.). *Education and Economic Development.* Chicago: Aldine, 1965.

ARENSBERG, CONRAD M., and NIEHOFF, ARTHUR H. *Introducing Social Change: A Manual for Americans Overseas.* Chicago: Aldine, 1964.

BYRNES, FRANCIS C. *Americans in Technical Assistance: A Study of Attitudes and Responses to Their Role Abroad.* New York: Frederick A. Praeger, 1965.

CLAWSON, MARION (ed.). *Natural Resources and International Development.* Baltimore, Md.: The Johns Hopkins Press, 1964.

CURRIE, LAUCHLIN. *Accelerating Development: The Necessity and the Means.* New York: McGraw-Hill, 1965.

DEWILDE, JOHN C., *et al. Experiences with Agricultural Development in Tropical Africa.* 2 vols. Baltimore, Md.: The Johns Hopkins Press, 1967.

EICHER, CARL K., and WITT, LAWRENCE W. (eds.). *Agriculture in Economic Development.* New York: McGraw-Hill, 1964.

ENKE, STEPHEN. *Economics for Development.* Englewood Cliffs, N.J.: Prentice-Hall, 1963.

Food and Agriculture Organization of the United Nations. *FAO in the Field.* Rome: FAO, 1965.

————. *The State of Food and Agriculture, Annual Report* (1967). Rome: FAO, 1967.

Ford Foundation. *A Richer Harvest, A Report on Ford Foundation Grants in Overseas Agriculture.* New York: Ford Foundation, Office of Reports, 1967.

————. *Tapestry for Tomorrow, The Ford Foundation Program in the Middle East.* New York: Ford Foundation, Office of Reports, 1964.

GALBRAITH, JOHN KENNETH. *Economic Development.* Cambridge, Mass.: Harvard University Press, 1964.

GEIGER, THEODORE. *The Conflicted Relationships: The West and the Transformation of Asia, Africa, and Latin America.* New York: Mc-Graw-Hill, 1967.

HENDRY, JAMES B. *The Small World of Khanh Hau. A Study of Economic Life and the Prospects of Development in a Vietnamese Rural Community.* Chicago: Aldine, 1964.

HIRSCHMAN, ALBERT O. *Development Projects Observed.* Washington, D.C.: The Brookings Institution, 1967.

————. *Journeys Toward Progress: Studies of Economic Policy-Making in Latin America.* New York: The Twentieth Century Fund, 1963.

HOROWITZ, DAVID. *Hemispheres North and South: Economic Disparity Among Nations.* Baltimore, Md.: The Johns Hopkins Press, 1966.

Iowa State University Center for Agricultural and Economic Development. *Alternatives for Balancing World Food Production Needs.* Ames, Iowa: Iowa State University Press, 1967. Papers presented at a conference on this subject.

————. *Food: One Tool in International Economic Development.* Ames, Iowa: Iowa State University Press, 1963.

JOHNSON, HARRY G. *Economic Policies Toward Less Developed Countries.* Washington, D.C.: The Brookings Institution, 1967.

McGOVERN, GEORGE S. *War Against Want: America's Food for Peace Program.* New York: Walker & Co., 1964.

MELLON, JOHN W. *The Economics of Agricultural Development.* Ithaca, N.Y.: Cornell University Press, 1966.

MILLIKAN, MAX F., and HAPGOOD, DAVID. *No Easy Harvest: The Dilemma of Agriculture in Underdeveloped Countries.* Boston: Little, Brown and Co., 1967.

MOOMAW, I. W. *The Challenge of Hunger: A Program for More Effective Foreign Aid.* New York: Frederick A. Praeger, 1965.

————. *Crusade Against Hunger.* New York: Harper & Row, 1966. This book presents the story of agricultural missionaries.

MOSEMAN, ALBERT H. (ed.). *Agricultural Sciences for the Developing Nations.* Washington, D.C.: American Association for the Advancement of Science, 1964.

MOSHER, ARTHUR T. *Getting Agriculture Moving: Essentials for Devel-*

opment and Modernization. New York: Frederick A. Praeger, 1966. Two volumes of readings, a collection of case studies, and a training manual are available from The Agricultural Development Council in New York.

MYRDAL, GUNNAR. *Challenge to Affluence.* New York: Vintage Books, 1963.

NAIR, KUSUM. *Blossoms in the Dust: The Human Factor in Indian Development.* New York: Frederick A. Praeger, 1962.

Organization for Economic Cooperation and Development. *Low Incomes in Agriculture—Problems and Policies.* Paris: OECD Publications, 1964.

PADDOCK, WILLIAM and PAUL. *Famine—1975: America's Decision, Who Will Survive?* Boston: Little Brown and Co., 1967.

———. *Hungry Nations.* Boston: Little, Brown and Co., 1964.

PEPELASIS, ADAMANTIOS A., MEARS, LEON, and ADELMAN, IRMA. *Economic Development: Analysis and Case Studies.* New York: Harper & Brothers, 1961.

RAWSON, ROBERT R. *The Monsoon Lands of Asia.* Chicago: Aldine, 1963.

ROSTOW, WALT W. *The Stages of Economic Growth.* New York: Cambridge University Press, 1960.

SCHULTZ, THEODORE W. *Economic Crises in World Agriculture.* Ann Arbor, Mich.: University of Michigan Press, 1965.

———. *Transforming Traditional Agriculture.* New Haven, Conn.: Yale University Press, 1964.

SEN, SAMAR R. *Strategy for Agricultural Development and Other Essays on Economic Policy and Planning.* 2d Ed. New York: Asia Publishing House, 1966.

SINAUER, ERNST M. *The Role of Communication in International Training and Education.* New York: Frederick A. Praeger, 1967.

SOUTHWORTH, HERMAN M., and JOHNSTON, BRUCE F. (eds.). *Agricultural Development and Economic Growth.* Ithaca, N.Y.: Cornell University Press, 1967.

STAKMAN, E. C., BRADFIELD, RICHARD, and MANGELSDORF, PAUL C. *Campaigns Against Hunger.* Cambridge, Mass.: Harvard University Press, 1967. This is an account of The Rockefeller Foundation agricultural programs.

TOMA, PETER A. *The Politics of Food for Peace.* Tucson, Ariz.: University of Arizona Press, 1967.

United Nations Education, Scientific, and Cultural Organization. *Education and Agricultural Development.* (Freedom from Hunger Campaign, Basic Study No. 15.) Paris: UNESCO, 1964.

WATERSTON, ALBERT. *Development Planning: Lessons of Experience.* Baltimore, Md.: The Johns Hopkins Press, 1965.

WHITEFORD, ANDREW H. (ed.). *A Reappraisal of Economic Development.* Chicago: Aldine, 1967. Papers presented at the Third Biennial Midwest Research Conference on Underdeveloped Areas.

WISER, WILLIAM H. and CHARLOTTE V. *Behind Mud Walls, 1930–1960.* Berkeley, Calif.: University of California Press, 1963.

Government Publications

ABEL, MARTIN E., and ROJKO, ANTHONY S. *World Food Situation, Prospects for World Grain Production, Consumption and Trade. Foreign Agricultural Economic Report No. 35.* U.S. Department of Agriculture. Washington, D.C.: U.S. Government Printing Office, 1967.

Agriculture and Economic Growth. Agricultural Economic Report No. 28. Washington, D.C.: U.S. Government Printing Office, 1963.

BROWN, LESTER R. *Increasing World Food Output, Problems and Prospects. Foreign Agricultural Economic Report No. 25.* U.S. Department of Agriculture. Washington, D.C.: U.S. Government Printing Office, 1965.

————. *Man, Land and Food, Looking Ahead at World Food Needs. Foreign Agricultural Economic Report No. 11.* U.S. Department of Agriculture. Washington, D.C.: U.S. Government Printing Office, 1963.

Changes in Agriculture in 26 Developing Nations, 1948 to 1963. Foreign Agricultural Economic Report No. 27. Washington, D.C.: U.S. Department of Agriculture, 1965.

CHRISTENSEN, RAYMOND P., HENDRIX, WILLIAM F., and STEVENS, ROBERT D. *How the United States Improved Its Agriculture. ERS Foreign No. 76.* Washington, D.C.: U.S. Department of Agriculture, 1964.

Farmer's World. (The Yearbook of Agriculture, 1964.) Washington, D.C.: U.S. Government Printing Office, 1964.

WEST, QUENTIN M. *World Food Needs.* Washington, D.C.: U.S. Department of Agriculture, February 16, 1966.

The World Food Budget 1970. Foreign Agricultural Economic Report No. 19. Washington, D.C.: U.S. Department of Agriculture, 1964.

The World Food Problem, A Report of the President's Science Advisory Committee, Panel on the World Food Supply. Washington, D.C.: U.S. Government Printing Office, 1967.

Periodicals

Economic Development and Cultural Change. Published quarterly by the University of Chicago Press.

FAO Review. Published bimonthly by the Food and Agriculture Organization of the United Nations, Rome.

Foreign Agriculture. Includes data on foreign crops and markets. Published weekly by the Foreign Agricultural Service of the U.S.D.A., Washington, D.C.

International Development Review. Published quarterly by the Society for International Development, Washington, D.C.

War on Hunger. A report from the Agency for International Development. Published monthly by the Office of War on Hunger of the AID, Washington, D.C.

Index